i

Come Home, Child

by David Robert Bayard

First Published May 14, 2020

Copyright by Skyboy Press | Kansas City, Missouri in 2022

International Standard Book Number (ISBN) 978-1-7349577-2-3

Front and back cover art by David Bayard and Jadyn Vannoy
All other photographs and illustrations by David Bayard

Also by David Bayard from Skyboy Press:

"Gathering the Self: Poems of the Heart" © 2018
"Haiku, Schmaiku and Headin' Out to Sea" © 2019
"In Nature's Image" © 2020
"Sky Stories: The Sky and Nature Calendar" published annually since 2015

All publications available at www.skyboyphotos.com

Skyboy Press
3201 Martha Truman Road
Kansas City, Missouri 64137
(816) 765-0080

Contents

Outside the window the sky is a gauzy film behind bare trees, uniform, featureless, waiting. As I watch, thin needles of rain begin stitching themselves down through the blanket of air until I hear the first drops patter pattering upon the skylight.

I see a single raindrop slowly jerking side to side, skittering drunk. Soon I see another. Then two, ten, then dozens. I realize it is snowing. A delightful scene!

Inside the warm, enclosed in the soft whisper of flakes shuffling across the window, I sit. The bare page of my notebook stares at me in reproach, uniform, featureless, waiting.

Inside my body, my head is screaming to stop writing, giving ten thousand reasons this is a bad idea. It'll do no good. Don't air dirty laundry. Nobody wants to read it. What does it matter anyway? Water under the bridge. Don't make a big deal of it. Bygones be. There are many others worse off than you. Don't rock the boat. You'll make your parents cry.

Heart is stopped, awaits decision. Belly tumbles like a washer with an unbalanced load, liquid gurgles and squirts of turmoil complaining. Arm holds rigid hand suspended over page. Fingers clench around the impotent fountain pen.

After some time I lay back. Open my chest, allow a deep sigh gather to bosom, eyes to close. I relax into the seat cushion. I recall the reason I began writing this.

I must tell the story. Even if only to myself.

The words come gushing forth like blood from a deep wound. Outside the snowfall deepens.

x

Falling

Yoo-hoo! Up here in the pine tree!

Wait, I'll swing back and forth on the tree so you can see me. Here I am! Come on up. Don't worry, it's pretty easy once you get up on the first few branches.

You made it! Isn't this great? Here, let's swing together on our two trees. Ready? Go!

Whoooh-weeee!

Isn't this fun? From up here you can see all the way to forever. And I love the wind. Look how it toussles your hair! It's a lot stronger than on the ground.

I'm so glad you could come. I've been here all by myself for a long, long time. Now I can tell you my story.

Let's climb down and I'll show you a bunch of other stuff. Watch out, that limb's kinda punk! There you go. It's a lot harder than climbing up, isn't it? That's what my cat says, anyway.

Now we're on the ground, let's go through the woods to the field in back. Follow me.

See how big it is out here? Here, now grab you one of these tall grasses, snap it off right at the ground--there you go--you can hold it like a spear, like you're an athlete or maybe a warrior in battle or something. Now, put your arm way, way back and throw!

Ooh, that was nice! Let me try one.

Wow, mine went almost as far! See, these tassels on the end make them soar really straight for a long, long time.

I feel so free here! Everything is warm and wraps around you like a blanket and you're as big as the whole world. The pine trees and the woods and the field with the birds and the sound of cicadas and the tall pampas grass rippling in the wind and the blue sky and the yellow sun—it's all alive and it's all happy!

I have an idea. Let's go to the front yard and lie down on the lawn. It's alright, you don't get bit by bugs or anything.

Here, this is nice. We don't have to move or do anything, just let the ground kind of pillow us.

I'm usually pretty shy, but somehow I'm not with you. I'm glad. I have a few friends but no one I can really talk to like this. Let's just lie here on the grass and dream, okay?

I haven't told this to anyone else, but I have a special place I like to go, inside my head.

My favorite time is after bedtime. I'm supposed to go right to sleep. But I like to read so I get into bed with a flashlight and pull the covers over my head. That way mom and dad don't know I'm awake. Then sometimes after I'm done reading, I close my eyes and go to my special place.

When you're there, you're just sort of hanging floating with no air or gravity. But don't worry, you can still breathe. There are lots of purple parakeets with rockets on their feet who go zooming around. And other birds, too, all different colors and shapes. And when you want to, you can put rockets on your own feet. You just think about them and bingo! There they are. Then you can go zooming around anywhere you want.

And there are funny green stars in the sky that jiggle like jumping beans. Sometimes they fall down. Or maybe they hit another star. Then they explode with a great big light. But no sound, remember? Because there's no air there.

And there's other planets going around all the stars, and if you put your rocket feet on and zoom way, way out you can explore them. Some are like ours, but most of them are really different. Sometimes there are no people on them, just animals, and sometimes only plants, and sometimes, things you've never seen before.

One time when I was out there I was thinking up a new planet. I knew just what it should look like, so I wished it were there. Then suddenly it was! I got to fly around and explore it. I guess I just made it up into being.

Ooh, and guess what? One time, I saw this girl doing pretty loops and swoops and swirls on her rocket feet, flying all over the place. I want to go see if I can find her again. Because I wouldn't mind if she maybe flew by me. I really wouldn't. Especially if she wanted to. That would be even better. I get a funny tingle just thinking about it.

Oh, look, the sun's going down, I lost track of time. It's okay, though, because now if we wait a little while we can see the night sky and I can show you how I leave the earth. Really! But we have to wait till our eyes adjust to the dark, so let's just close them and listen. If we're real quiet, we can hear all the sounds that happen when it's quiet. The grass whispering and the wind talking to the trees and the worms digging down below us.

Okay, I think it's dark enough now. Open your eyes.

Look at all the stars! It's like we're not in the front yard anymore, or even on earth! We're just floating around on this little chunk of grass and dirt and rocks and bugs all by ourselves in the middle of nowhere. It's even better than my special space! Because it's real. And because we can both see it.

I like being here with you.

Ooh, did you see that falling star! And there's another! Wow! And you can see the Milky Way, too. See that big batch of skim milk that got spilled out all over the stars? That's it. My dad says it's the big, big galaxy we all live in.

Let's just let ourselves go farther and farther out until we're way out there, floating in this wonderful dark space with stars and planets and galaxies. Way away from everything.

Here's what happened to me a long, long time ago, or maybe even before that. Way back as far as I remember.

I was just a kid then, not like now. I'm almost six. Anyway, I was on my big tricycle, bigger than me. It was nice and warm outside, and I knew the sun was what was making it warm. So I looked up and sure enough, there it was exactly over my head.

Then I wondered if the sun was everywhere or just right above me. So I rode my tricycle all the way to where the world ended, almost five houses away. Then I stopped and I looked up again, and guess what? The sun was still right over my head!

Then I rode back past the house the other way, this time for more houses than I could even count to where things ended on the other side. I looked up. The sun was still in the same place.

I couldn't figure out why it didn't move. Because when I'm in my room at home with the light over my head, when I move, it moves back the other way. But the sun didn't do that. Maybe it's not tied to the sky the same way my light is tied to the ceiling. Maybe it can follow me around.

But that didn't seem right. My dad says everything works the same everywhere in the universe. And he knows a lot. Maybe everything there is to know. So, the sun must work the same as the light in my bedroom. It must be moving backward when I move, too. But it didn't.

I thought about this for a long, long time. Then suddenly it dawned on me that if it's farther away than my light, it would move slower. And if it's a lot farther away, it would move even slower. And if it was far enough away, I wouldn't be able to see it move at all.

Which I couldn't.

So that meant it must be way farther away than the world down here, which is only maybe two times five houses. It must be almost a finity gillion houses away!

The more I thought about it, the more excited I got. Because if the sun wasn't following me, it meant I wasn't the center of the universe, which was good, because if I was, I'd have to be in charge of everything and I don't want to be. I could just be a kid and let everything take care of itself.

But it also means if the universe is that big, there's a lot of room in it for me and you and everybody else, and for all kinds of places to go and things to do. My dad says I can do anything I want to if I want it bad enough. I want to try all kind of things and have all sorts of adventures and see what there is out there for me. It's like my special imaginary place would become real!

Wanna come with me?

Sometimes my mom reads Winnie-the-Pooh to me. I really like the silly things the bear does! And all the other animals are funny and quirky and get into all sorts of adventures.

She gave me a book of Greek mythology that I really like. I thought it would be hard to read but it's not. I couldn't stop, the stories were so much fun. People back then were just like us, only different. There were gods, too, but they acted the same as people, except they had super-powers. And sometimes they did really bad stuff!

I got Tarzan of the Apes for my birthday, and then I read The Count of Monte Cristo, and Tom Swift, Space Cadet. He flies in space and invents really cool stuff and does incredible things with science and stuff.

Sometimes when my mom reads to me, I look up at the book-shelf and dream of adventures I want to have and exciting things I want to do, being happy and sad and brave and cowardly and noble and vengeful and passionate and devious and lost and found and bold and timid--I mean, all those things that people are in the books.

I feel warm inside when my mom reads to me. Because then I know she likes me.

I'm not sure if she always does, though. When she's reading to me or watching me play in the living room or we're out in the garden together, I think she loves me. But when she tells me to do stuff like empty the garbage, or clean up my room, well, she sounds like she's a little mad at me. I guess she loves me then, too. But her face gets harder and tighter and I get scared.

And sometimes she gets a faraway look on her face like she's gone away somewhere, I don't know where. It's like when you're watching a show on TV but then someone turns it off and you never find out how the story ends? It's sort of like that. She looks like she's right in front of me but somehow she's really not.

Then I get all in a panic because I don't know how she feels. My tummy gets tight and I try to figure out what to do to make her like me again.

Then pretty soon I don't even like me!

That's when I go to my room or outside in the woods or put my hands in front of my eyes to go to my special space.

Mom and dad were out in the front yard yesterday working on the new brick patio. My dad asked me to come out and help. I didn't want to because I was doing something else but I went anyway.

He showed me how to lay new bricks and tamp them down in the sand with a rubber mallet so they would all be the same height. Then he had me do one by myself.

I tried but I couldn't get it to line up with the other bricks. He came over and showed me how when that happens, you have to take the brick back out, put more sand under it and try again. So I did. But then it was too high, so I lifted it up and took out some sand and put it back. Now it was too low! I tried this a bunch of times until finally I got it maybe right.

So I put in another brick and got it level. I thought it was okay, so I told him I was done.

He came over and looked. "This is not the herringbone pattern," he said. He pointed to the rest of the bricks. "I told you about that. Do you remember?"

"I think so." But I didn't, really.

"Well, that's not right. See how every other brick is sideways?"

Now I saw what he meant. "Yes."

"You'll have to take that brick out and redo it."

So I did, but there was a bunch of grass there now and I couldn't get it level. I dug the grass out, put the brick back, and finally got it sort of flat. I put another brick in, this time at the right angle. Then I did a bunch of more bricks. After a while he came over and looked.

"What did I say about the herringbone pattern?" he asked. He sounded upset so I didn't say anything. "Look at the first brick you did. See?" And then I could tell I'd turned the very first one the wrong way sideways, six bricks ago! "You'll have to tear all this out and do it over."

So then I took them all out again but I was so upset by then that nothing seemed to work and the sand was uneven and the bricks were all over and every time I put one in it bumped the one behind it and I started getting really frustrated. I started to cry a little bit and that made everything worse. He finally came over then and looked at what I did.

Then he turned to my mom and said, "Everything he touches turns to shit!"

I never ever heard my dad say that word before! I don't know what it means, but I think it's bad.

Suddenly I didn't want to be there anymore. My tummy hurt and I started really crying because he was mad at me, and I had messed everything up, but I tried to be quiet so he wouldn't hear me cry. I went back inside the house and went up to my room and closed the door.

Then today I did something bad again.

My dad asked me to help him in his shop. He was working on his old car, what we called the Grey Ghost, an old-timey car with a circle room in the back for gangsters. He was fixing up to be like new.

"Do I have to?" It just came right out! I didn't mean it to. He didn't say anything, he just went over to the car and started tinkering on the dashboard. I thought he was mad so I started to say, "Wait, I'll help you!" but I couldn't get the words out. I just stood there. Then after a while I went to the living room to play with the cardboard racetrack I was building.

Later my mom came down with her face all scrunched up. "David, what happened? You made your father cry."

I didn't mean to! I guess I should have said yes when dad asked me. I've got to be careful not to make him cry again. I don't remember what I said to mom. I went up to my room again and hid.

Later my mom walked by and saw me through the open door. She came in and asked me if anything was wrong.

"I don't know. I guess I'm sort of sad."

"What are you sad about?"

I couldn't tell her why because I didn't want to make my dad cry again. "I just am. I guess."

"I'm sorry, honey. Maybe if you go outside and play in the back yard, that'll make you feel better. You like playing out there, don't you?" It's true, I do like being in the woods and throwing my spears of pampas grass and playing Tarzan the Ape Man.

"I guess so, mom."

"Okay, then. Go have fun!"

She left but I just stayed there. When she tells me to do stuff like that, even if it's stuff I already like to do, then all of a sudden I don't want to anymore.

Later I did go out to the back yard woods and tried throwing my pampas grass spears but it wasn't the same. So, I started yelling the Tarzan yell I like to do. Not the fake one the guy does in the movie that sounds like a Billy goat with a sore throat, but a full, deep, fierce animal challenge that curdles your blood and freezes your bones and makes the hairs on the back of your neck stand at attention, like what I imagined inside my head when I read the real Tarzan of the Apes books.

Then at the end of that long, long yell, when I had gotten it all out, I plunked down there in the tall waving grass and I cried and cried and I just couldn't stop crying.

Did I tell you I'm in school? I am. I'm a lot older now, too.

I've been going for almost a year now. I think I like it, but maybe not. Something happened yesterday you could help me with, okay?

The teacher made each of us send a Valentine card to someone else in the class. I got a card from Becky. She wears a brown dress. She's nice.

Her card looked like this inside:

David, if you like me,

then the feeling is mutual.

She wrote my name! I liked that. I looked up and there she was across the room staring right at me. But then I looked down and pretended to read the card again. Because I didn't know what to do.

Because I don't know what the word "mutual" means!

Do you? Is it bad? Because I don't think I'm supposed to like girls. My mom and dad don't know about me liking girls. They never talk about it, so I never talk about it. It's sort of a secret. And I think secrets are bad.

If it was mutual that I liked Becky, then I might be in trouble. Because I kind of do. Like her. But I didn't look at her any more for the rest of the day or the rest of the week.

But what if mutual was a good thing? That's why I'm asking. Because if it is, I think it would maybe make me tingle inside like when the girl with rocket feet flies by. I feel it right now, in fact, just thinking about her liking me, and it being a good thing. Wow, it feels nice! When I get home, I'm going to go inside my room and think about it.

Sometimes I wish I was somebody else so I wouldn't have to be so confused.

I'm back in my special space now. It's cozy in here. I don't see the girl with rocket feet but I've been exploring a lot of new places besides the ones I told you about.

I thought about making up a new planet again and it worked! You just go relaxed and stop doing anything, even thinking about doing anything, just be still and let yourself sort of fall away into your inside where your eyes can't go. Slow and quick at the same time, like Peter Pan trying to catch his shadow. Then whatever you want to happen, happens! I'm still trying to get the hang of it.

But be careful because there are corners inside the space where it's a little dark and hard to see. Places I didn't make up. There's a black lake I saw once that has no bottom. I don't know what's in there. I jumped in one time but I was scared of what might be down there in the water. Weird things could slither around or bite me or even pull me down. I don't go swimming there. But I'm curious. Maybe if I feel brave, I'll jump in again.

But when you're in the space and scary stuff happens, it's okay. Don't worry. You just wake up and then you're back in the real world.

Hi, I'm back again after another long long time.

I just started seventh grade this year. I like a lot of my classes, especially science and math. My dad is a scientist. He knows a lot of really exciting stuff.

My favorite class is Chemistry. I like how everything works so perfectly. Whenever you put sodium (Na) together with chlorine (Cl), it comes out NaCl, which is salt! And it does it every time, and it always works, and it never doesn't work. I wish everything were like that, where you knew what would happen when you did things.

I like doing chemistry in the lab at school so much, I thought I could set up my very own lab at home! So, I found a place under the stairs in the basement that's perfect. There's lots of room down there, and I figured out how I would set it up. The test tubes and beakers and a Bunsen burner and a few pipettes and stuff on a countertop, then all the chemicals underneath.

I asked my dad if was okay.

"I don't want you doing that down there," he said.

"In the front, right under the stairs? There's lots of room there, okay, dad?" I asked.

"I'd rather we set it up in the main workshop. We'll find some space there." He led me into his shop that had the lathe and drill press and saws and all the tools. He looked around and thought for a while. Then he said, "Why don't you use these four drawers?" He went to the end of his fifteen-foot-long bench, the last stack of drawers. He opened one and started taking his stuff out. "You can work on the countertop here with your experiments. What do you think?"

I was disappointed. I had my heart set on a lab in the basement, a place of my very own. Where I could just be by myself. But I didn't say anything, I just stood there.

He finished emptying the drawers. I went ahead and started setting up my stuff. The next week I did an experiment. It wasn't as much fun as it was at school. Then he came into the shop to do some work of his own. "What are you up to?" he asked.

I was embarrassed. "I'm mixing sodium hydroxide and copper sulfate. It's supposed to precipitate into something."

"Sounds interesting. Why don't you start keeping a record of the experiments? Then you can see how they compare with each other."

"Okay," I said

"There's some notepaper in the drawer over here. Do you want me to help?"

"No, that's okay. I can do it." I didn't do it.

He went back to his side of the bench and started drilling something.

I couldn't even think anymore. I sat there getting more and more upset because this wasn't fun. I wasn't even sure if I liked chemistry anymore. After sitting there for a while, I started sneaking my chemicals and stuff back into the drawers so he wouldn't know I was quitting. Then I went upstairs to be by myself.

Later my mom walked by my room. Sometimes when she walks by, she'll see me and come on in to tell me something or ask me something. I never know whether she will or not.

This time she came in. "What's going on, honey?" I guess she could see I was upset.

"I don't know, I'm just sad. My chemistry experiment didn't come out like I thought." I was mad, too, but didn't tell her that, or about me wanting my own chemistry lab or about dad being in the shop or anything else. I thought it might make him cry.

"You know, your mind is really powerful. Whatever it is you feel, you're deciding to feel that way. You're making that decision on your own. I think if you just make up your mind not to be sad, you can change how you feel."

She's a psychologist. She knows lots of stuff like this.

"I have a theory that everything in the universe is what we make it. We can live as if it's all outside of us, but really, we are creating it ourselves. We hold responsibility for it. So, if you just decide you want to be happy, you can just be happy."

She talked some more, and then some more, then I guess I was okay because she left the room. I tried to think about what she said.

I thought to myself: if I want to badly enough, and really focus on it, I can make myself not be sad. I had to be brave and strong.

So I tried it and it sort of worked, I think. I felt a little bit better. Maybe I just thought I did, but isn't that the same thing? Because what you think you feel is what you make yourself feel? I don't know how to tell. Or maybe I didn't try hard enough because I think I felt even sadder than I was before.

After that my head hurt and I had to go take some aspirin.

I went down to dinner that night and mom was setting the table and she didn't say anything more about it. And I didn't say anything, so neither of us said anything. I just wanted to hide. I didn't want to have to be okay and stuff, I just wanted to run away and be how I was being, all by myself, so I wouldn't have to see anybody. I didn't even care if I went hungry.

It's the next day now and already I feel better. I figured out some things I can do to make up for making dad cry. I'll do better. I'm going to try real hard. I'm going to knuckle down and straighten up and fly right, like he says. I'll be like Spartacus in the books, all strong and noble and fearless and stuff. You'll see.

But I'm scared now. I didn't know I was scared till I thought about seeing dad again without making him cry and then I got scared. And then made myself feel bad, I guess.

God, I feel awful! I'm so lost and alone I can't stand it.

It always feels like I'm hungry but I don't know for what. And I walk around just really sad all the time. I try not to be but I still am. I don't know what's wrong with me. Every time I try to figure it out, I just go deeper farther down sadder. I hate myself!

And another thing. Sometimes I start crying for no reason.

It's not logical. I'll be normal and then all of a sudden, I'm crying! I guess mom would say I should be able to figure it out and make myself happy, but I can't. There must be a way I can stop feeling like this.

I wish somebody would hug me. Really, really hug me, real close, almost like we're the same person. For a long, long time. And not try to pull away. I wish I could just say or do or be or talk about anything I wanted, and I could even cry if I wanted to or laugh or be mad and nobody would try to figure me out or make me different or tell me not to cry. And they wouldn't be disgusted with me or think I was bad, no matter what I did, or try to change me or make me into a better person. They would just keep on hugging me and loving me just the way I am.

Sometimes I dream about someone, a girl mostly, who would just keep on hugging me like that. I'm dreaming about that right now. Someone who would never stop loving me and never, ever go away.

I don't know if there is anybody like that. Maybe it's just angels in fairy tales and stuff.

Sometimes in bed at night I dream of her coming down over me and hovering there over me and then dropping down slowly, softly, gently, and then wrapping her whole entire body around me. It feels so good and warm and delicious even thinking about it.

In fact, I'm in my space right now, under the covers in my bed, dreaming the angel is right next to me on the pillow. It feels so good. Don't tell mommy where I am, though, okay? If she finds out, she'll probably come in and tell me how I can feel again.

Uh-oh, here she comes. I've gotta pull off my skin and let her in.

I mean, not really, but that's how it feels sometimes. She comes in my room whenever she wants. I can't pretend to be sleeping this time because I'm not. I think she wants me to do something. I have to go away now, okay? I probably won't be able to get back here for a while. I'll be back as soon as I've done whatever she wants. Please don't go away! Promise?

Today I got this idea about time travel. I got out my journal and wrote to the David who is me in the future. I told him where I would be tomorrow at 10:00 AM in the morning. Right here in my room upstairs in my house on South Park Road in Bethel Park, Pennsylvania, United States of America, Planet Earth, Solar System, Outer Rim of the Milky Way, and (so he wouldn't miss me by mistake and go zooming by), within the Local Group, which is a few parsecs from the Small and Large Magellanic Clouds. Then I tucked my journal away in a safe place.

Tomorrow morning is Saturday. I don't have any chores to do or stuff. Tonight I'm going to go get some rye-bread toast and butter it on both sides and a glass of orange juice and my journal where I told him when and where to come and get under the covers in bed and read my Uncle Scrooge and Donald Duck comic books and dream about it. Then tomorrow I'll be here at ten o'clock sharp to meet him.

I hope he can help me get out of the dark places when I'm stuck in there. I hope he can show me how to get rid of the feelings. Because by then he--I mean I--will have figured out a lot of this stuff? Won't he? I hope he can save me. It really hurts. I don't want to have to feel this anymore.

Well, it's Saturday afternoon now and it didn't work. The future me never showed up. I waited and waited but it didn't make sense to wait too long, because if you are coming back to a specific point in time, how hard can that be?

I tried to figure out why he didn't come but I couldn't. Time paradoxes are one possibility. Maybe that would wreck space-time. But I know I would eventually figure a way around that, so that's not it. What if I never invent time travel? I considered that too, but then, I can do anything I put my mind to if I try hard enough. That's what my dad says.

All I'm left with is that I will stop caring enough to come back and save myself. And that's the scariest of all.

I hope he still comes. Because now I'm stuck here. Sometimes I feel desperate. It's like there's something very bad and wrong inside me and I don't know how to get rid of it.

Mom took me to see a psychologist this week to see if he could figure out why I was so sad all the time. We went downtown to Pittsburgh where he had an office. When we got there, he asked my mom if he could talk to me alone. She said yes, so I went into his office while mom waited outside.

He had a big soft stuffed armchair that you could just sink into, so I sat and sank. We chatted a little bit and then he asked about me and mom in a way that I think was supposed to be just between the two of us.

I didn't know what to say. I told him I liked her and all. I said she reads books to me, and helps me with my English homework, and she sometimes watches me playing outside. And how she peeks into my room sometimes and always asks how I'm doing.

We talked a little bit more, then he changed the subject and asked me why I was running. I wasn't! I was just sitting right there in his big stuffed armchair!

I don't know if he helped me feel better that first time or not. I don't know how you're supposed to feel inside or even how you figure out how you feel. Maybe I'm not doing it right.

We went to him a couple more times, too. I hoped he would ask me why I was running again or tell me what he meant, but he never did. I told him about my science experiments and model rockets and stuff. And my friend, and how we were going to go to the stars together when we grew up. Then that was it.

But one time was a little different. He started asking me about stuff I didn't get. We'd been talking about mom, and he said something like, do I know why I've been so sad? I said I didn't.

Then he said, "Yes, you do." But I didn't! I don't even remember how that time ended. I guess I'll have to go back to him some more to figure it out. That's what mom says I should do. She says it's for my own good, in the end, so I guess I'll stick it out.

I don't know if I feel better after all that or not. I feel all weird inside. I hope my future self can still get here. Maybe he just got the time wrong.

I always like myself better in the morning. I like the sun coming up and the early dawn light, the way it lifts everything up to brighter than it is. It feels like anything can happen.

I want to have great adventures and go to the stars and be a great actor and be sad and happy and mad and blissful and fall in love and kiss a girl and do science and write a book and cook a feast and invent time travel and become a hermit, I mean, everything you can do! I can't wait.

When my mom talks to me about all the adventures I could be doing, and how fun and wonderful everything will be, she gets really excited. Then I feel excited, too. But you know, later when I'm trying to really do it, have all these grand adventures all at once, I get confused and scared and it's not the same as I imagined. It's no fun. What's wrong with me? Why can't I just be like I'm supposed to be?

Sometimes I want to go far away in the woods somewhere and just lie down in the dirt and let the mud be all over me and animals eat me and stuff and just let everything happen to me that can happen to me. I don't care anymore!

Except I get scared when I think about really doing it. I probably couldn't even do that right.

Well, it's a lot later now. I'm still in school, but it's high school now, which is bigger. I'm bigger, too.

In the morning for homeroom everyone stands in the lobby before class starts. I stand in the corner with three other kids. They're all in one of my science or math classes. None of the other students wants to be with us.

I'm always holding my stomach in so people will think I'm

like the cool kids in school. But inside I feel bad. I think everybody can see how I feel inside. Maybe they feel the same way I do. Probably not.

Maybe the three guys I stand with do, but I'm too afraid to ask them so we just stand around in the lobby together and talk about stuff.

I like my English class. The teacher makes me want to write well. (It's 'well' by the way, not 'good'! Haha!) She reads what I wrote. Then we talk about it, and she tells me what she likes about my writing and the ways I could make it even better. She never says anyone's writing is bad. I like that. To think nothing I do is bad, it can maybe be done better but it's all good.

We're studying Julius Caesar. I like Shakespeare. Everything he says is so majestic! Someday I want to write like he does. "You blocks, you stones, you worse than senseless things!" He shows how complicated people are, how everyone's got some secret life and we're all scheming for something or other.

Like how Mark Anthony really wants to be Caesar, but he pretends he doesn't. He tells the crowd that and they swoon. Swoon! What a word! Then he keeps going on about how he's no big deal, he'd make a lousy Caesar, but the more he says it, the more they want him to be Caesar. And it works! They vote for him.

All the plays are great, Shakespeare shows how full of contradictions people are, that nobody is all good or all bad but a mix of both. I wonder what it would be like to see myself from the outside like that, like a character in a book, instead of being stuck here inside blind to my foibles?

Then in Hamlet: "There are more things in heaven and earth, Horatio, than are dreamt of in your philosophy." Wow. That line really got to me. Look beneath the surface, he says, there's a whole world there that you can't even see.

But I don't get the rest of Hamlet quite so much, why he's always quiet and mouse-like, hiding, after his uncle kills his dad. Why does he let him just run around and do whatever he wants and get away with it? Why doesn't he just get him? He should just be brave and do something!

It's like he's just supposed to stand there and not do anything. Just stand there and take it!

I'd never be like that.

Something I don't like about high school, though. The kids tease me about the way my ribs stick in instead of out. All the other boys' ribs stick out, like Superman's, real strong and stuff. But mine don't do that, they sort of stick in. The kids call me "sunken chest", like a pirate's treasure or something. I feel bad I'm this way. I should work harder to make it different, but I don't know how, so I just hide and try to pull my stomach in.

Then there's this kid who stands in front of me in the middle of the walkway every day between classes and starts hitting me. It really hurts. The first time I got dizzy and almost fell over. I dropped my books, the papers got scattered all over. And then while I was picking them up, feeling really mad and scared, he started calling me names and stuff. I got to class okay but my face was sore all day.

I told my mom about it when I got home.

"I'm so sorry, sweetie. The next time he does that, why don't you just bend over and run at him with your head down, butt him in the belly real hard? That'll knock the wind out of anybody."

So, the next day there he was again, and he stood in front of me, and I stood in front of him, and he hit me, and I just stood there sort of numb and stiff. I couldn't seem to move. I couldn't bend over with my head down like my mom said, even though I wanted to. So he just kept hitting me. Nobody else did anything either, everybody just kept walking on to their classes as if I weren't even there. I don't remember how it ended, I guess I picked up my books and went to class.

I guess I just have to go stand in front of him tomorrow, too, I don't have any choice. Maybe I'll get all tough and strong inside if I do that, like Spartacus. Maybe that's how Spartacus did it. I don't know. Maybe that's being strong.

I guess I'm just supposed to stand there and not do anything. Just stand there and take it.

Last year was my sophomore year and we went to Thailand where my dad had a job in physics working for the Thai government. We stayed a whole year and everything. It was really neat. We learned to speak the language and went to the international school there. We took trips around Thailand, saw elephants lifting heavy teak logs, went to Pataya down the coast from Bangkok and had a vacation on the beach. We did all sorts of fun things. Now we're back home.

There was a servant girl for the Thai family that lived across the street. I would see her sometimes when our family went over to visit. I liked her a lot. I think she liked me, too, but I never could ask her. Even though I wanted to. One time, somebody told me she didn't like being a servant and wanted to get away.

So I dreamed about going over and saving her and the two of us running away together. I thought about her all the time. Wimohn--that was her name. Even saying her name out loud, I get all excited and tingly.

Now we're back home. My high school looks a lot smaller, and the other kids seem strange and limited, after being in a different culture for so long. And now I'll never see Wimohn again. I'm lonely as heck.

I never told anybody what I'm about to tell you, okay? But you're someone I can talk to.

Last night I was writing in my journal about her, about Wimohn, and drawing pictures of her wearing a sarong, with her round straw hat tied under her chin, carrying a bundle slung over her shoulder. The writing made me tingle all over like the girl with rocket feet does. Except this was more real. And then I wrote some stuff and some more stuff and I drew some more pictures of her. Pretty soon I felt all delicious inside like good music and bright colors and sweet flowers make you feel.

Then suddenly I felt really bad! Worse than I've ever felt. I wasn't supposed to be doing this! I am a disgusting, horrible person for liking this. For enjoying it!

All night long I kept waking up and worrying and finally I couldn't stand it, I got up and went to my journal and went to those pages where all that stuff was and I put a ruler down real hard right there where I started doing that stuff and I tore the page right up to the part with all the pictures and the writing and stuff and I crumpled it up and threw it in the wastebasket and I did it so carefully that no one who ever reads my journal later would ever see what I'd done.

Then I went back to bed.

But I didn't feel better after I'd torn it out. I didn't feel anything. Just sort of blank, like there was nothing there to feel. But all twisted and tangled inside like the Gordian knot.

I'm in a bigger school now, a college way away from home, living in a dorm room with two other students.

I don't know if I want to be here or not. I picked engineering for my major. It's real hard, not as fun as I thought it would be. But I guess I just have to stay here now and try to figure it out. Dad said I could be anything I wanted when I grow up. Maybe I'm grown up already. I guess I want to be an engineer then. That's what I think he would want.

A couple days ago, though, I did something bad.

I was passing by another dorm room when most everyone was at class and the room was empty and there was this really cool turntable there. So, I went in and picked it up and with my chest thumping real loud I went back to my room and put it on my desk. I don't know why I did it.

I didn't think anybody saw me. But then the school people came into my room only two hours later and asked me if I took the turntable. I told them yes, I did. Because my dad said you never have to lie. But they got upset anyway and asked me why I did it. I told them I didn't know. Just like I told you.

I'm back home now because they have to decide if they want me in the school or not. They'll let us know in a month.

Meantime mom said I have to stay in her study off the hallway every day till then. Even weekends. It's this little cubicle just big enough to stretch my arms out wide, with only a desk and chair and typewriter and paper. I have stay there eight hours a day and keep up with my homework in case the school lets me back in.

That's where I am now. In this tiny room. But I deserve it. I was bad. I'm supposed to be doing homework right now, too, but I'm not. Instead I'm writing to you. I should be doing homework for the whole eight hours, so every time I'm not, I feel wrong inside. But right now, I'm glad you're here.

I can't get back into my space now, either. With the girl with rocket feet and the stars and the lake. I don't know why. And I'm having strange dreams.

Sometimes I'm in a house or basement and the walls start to close in, or maybe I'm following a tunnel somewhere and it ends, and when I turn back the way I came, it's all blocked off. I'm trapped. I start to panic, but then I wake up. Thank goodness it was only a bad dream!

One time I had this dream where I'm guarding a border with a rifle, like the American sector against the Russians. A woman comes up leading a tour group and she starts to walk past me. You can't cross the border! I shout. But they do anyway. She's leading the tour and she's chatting away to them and pays no attention to me whatsoever. It's like she can't hear me.

No, it's more like she doesn't care. They all just walk across the border like it's no big deal. It is! In the dream, I know I'm supposed to shoot them but I can't. I don't know what to do so I just let them come in and pretend to be okay with it. But inside I can feel myself boiling like acid.

I've got to go now. I've got to study. I'll let you know what happens, okay? Will you still be here?

Well, it's two weeks later now. The school said no, you can't come back. Now I have to go into the army. If I don't I'll get drafted because I'm not in school so it's better if I just join up.

It's scary. But you know the funny thing? I'm excited. I didn't think I would be but I am. I don't have a choice anyway. I feel kind of free, like I can just let go and let stuff happen to me and I can't do anything about it.

And I won't have to worry about Mom and Dad anymore because I'll be in the army. I like that. Even though I'm not supposed to.

I hope you can follow me from here on. If you want. It'll be an adventure together. Just you and me. Okay?

Wow! Have I been busy. I've had quite a few adventures since I saw you last. It feels like whole lifetimes!

I joined the army, and that was the longest three years of my life. That's why I couldn't talk to you because I had to stay in the army the whole time. I went to Korea for a year and patrolled the DMZ with my platoon. I had some hard times. I toughened up a lot. I feel older now but I still don't know if I'm grown up.

Then when I got out of the army I joined the circus. I got to set up the big tent and drive a semi-trailer. Then I joined the hippies on Haight Street. I played guitar and sang in a band. I hitchhiked across the country. And back. Twice. I traveled all over.

I fell in love, too. Then back out. Then back in with somebody else.

I had so many adventures I don't even know how to tell them all to you.

But you know what? They were nothing like I thought they'd be when I was a kid, lying on the bed with my mother reading about adventures and the two of us dreaming. The future's not the same as it was back then. I thought I'd feel all noble and courageous, remember? What I really felt most of the time was lost, lonely and scared.

In the Army, somebody died partly because of something I did. And it was real! It was hard to understand how I felt. I don't think about it anymore. I can't. I don't know what would happen if I did so I don't. I think I just put it away somewhere inaccessible where I don't have to ever see it again.

Then two months ago something happened. I'm still not sure what it was.

You remember that psychologist my mother took me so long ago? Well, he kept in touch with me and with her after that. He became more like a friend to me. I'd see or talk to him every couple of years. He helped me figure out my life out when I was stuck or confused.

Well, he had moved out to California, and that's where I was after the Army. He must have heard I was there, because one day he called out of the blue and invited me to come visit for dinner. So, I hitchhiked up to Marin County where he had a nice big house. When he met me at the door, he gave me a big hug.

He introduced me to his wife and showed me around the house. We chatted for a while. He offered me a glass of wine. That made me feel very adult.

His wife was making dinner. "Come and help me bake bread," he offered. "This is almost a spiritual thing with me now." We went to the kitchen, where he pulled a big lump of dough onto the countertop then dipped his hands in a flour bowl and started kneading.

"It's like a meditation. You use your hands, your whole body gets into it. It's a really visceral experience." He was grinning, shifting his weight back and forth. He and the bread moved together. Chunks of sticky dough and flour began flying in white sprays across the marble countertop. "See how it's starting to get stiff? It's not as wet. You have to keep adding flour and kneading, adding flour and kneading. Here, you try."

Soon my hands were covered in gooey dough. "That's it, fold it over and over again. Isn't this a deep body experience? You work with your hands and it's immediate. I'm doing more body work now, not so much talking therapy. This visceral kind of work is what people need, not some intellectual claptrap."

After dinner, his wife went off somewhere else while he and I went to the living room with another glass of wine. We sat and talked about life and psychology and philosophy and whatever we wanted to. I felt like I could say anything I wanted and it would be alright with him. He was like a god to me, then, so vibrant and alive and spiritual. I felt like a little puppy, soaking up his wisdom and knowledge.

He got up, went to the shelf to pull down a record and put it on his really nice turntable. "I want you to hear this," he called over his shoulder. "It's Bela Bartok. Why don't you lie down on the carpet while I get some more wine? I'll be right back. Just close your eyes and wait for the music. This is an incredible experience."

I lay on the floor, eyes closed, listening. A few clicks and pops, a faint whisper of violins starting on a simple four-note theme, then a rich weaving of sound overlapping the same earthy, sweet melody. The music was so crisp and clear it seemed to come from inside my head.

Suddenly a fierce crescendo cracked the room open, engulfed my body in crashing waves of joy and pain, despair and hope all tangled up together. I wept.

"Isn't this amazing?" he whispered. I jumped. He was lying right next to me. I hadn't heard him come back into the room. "This is my favorite concerto of his. Just listen to the sound!"

I relaxed and laid back. "Yeah, I love this. It's made me cry."

"Keep listening, it gets better. Just let the sound carry you."

I disappeared into the rhythms and the intricate play of sounds, drifting into a kind of meditation. This is when it happened. I gradually became aware that he was fiddling somehow with my pants. I lay still. Before I really knew or guessed what was happening, I realized he was doing something to me that I thought only girls did.

It was so strange and unexpected. I didn't know what to do. I froze. I didn't want it to stop because it felt good. But strange, wrong, weird. I just lay there helpless in a torment of pleasure all tangled up with confusion.

He pulled away, then whispered, "Let's go into the back bedroom." I became a deep form of nothingness. I got up and followed him robotically. He guided me to a small windowless room and onto a bed, coaxed me onto all fours. Then I felt him take off my pants, or pull them down, or I can't remember. I could hear Bartok faintly in the distance holding the walls up.

He left me there for a minute which was ten years. He came back, he came back, then from behind me he put himself inside me in a way that really hurt.

I thought sex was supposed to feel good. This didn't feel good. Or did it? Maybe this was it. I think he asked me how I felt, good, or maybe he didn't, or, but, what, did I say. What? Where was I. What was this thing happened. He got done, got up, got off, got away, I heard him say something, or he didn't, or maybe or the bedroom door closed or opened. The door opened. He left. Did he? Yes. Gone. But maybe still there maybe.

I was by myself alone and lost. And there I was in his house! I don't remember what I did or how I pulled my pants back up. If there was a window in that room, I would have crawled out of it.

I felt dirty but there was no way to clean myself.

I don't remember how I got out of the house, whether I saw him, or his wife, or said anything, or what happened after that.

I couldn't tell if what he did was good or bad. I couldn't tell how I felt about it, how I should feel, how I did feel, if I felt or didn't.

After that I stopped myself inside somehow. Until now, telling you. Now I'm thinking about it again. It was way down inside where I couldn't see it in a box I thought I never had to open again.

I was afraid you wouldn't like me if I told you and you'd go away. I am really glad you didn't.

Hi, I'm back again. I think I must be grown up now. I'm not sure. I can open my eyes wider than I ever could but there are still places inside I'm not able to see.

I haven't talked to my parents since the Army. I've been living with a roommate in an apartment about the size of my thumb.

Last month my mother somehow found out where I was living. And she must have figured out I was being a hippie. She thought that meant I was taking drugs. And she was right.

One day I got a call. "Hi, sweetie, I'm in San Francisco today and I'd love to see you if you have some time."

"Oh, hi. Mom? Is that you?"

"Yes, honey."

"Wow. What...how come you're here?"

"I'm attending the convention of the national psychology association. It's only a one-day event. I've got to go back tomorrow. But I do have a little time this morning before the seminars. Do you want to meet me for breakfast?"

"Well, sure, I guess. I mean, I'd love to. Where are you? Should I come meet you? Where do you want to go?" Words tumbled out before thought.

"Why don't you decide, honey? I don't know this city very well."

"Oh," I offered. "Okay. Just a minute." I put my hand over the phone. "Jon, it's my mom."

"What the...?"

"I know! She wants to meet me for breakfast."

"That's crazy, David. You haven't seen her for what, years? And you said you didn't really want to. Did she tell you she was coming?"

"No, but I think it's okay. She said she has to go back tomorrow."

"It's weird she's just now telling you she's here," he wondered.

"I guess so. Maybe she didn't have time."

"So, what do you want to do?"

"I guess I'll go to breakfast with her."

"Well..." He wore the look he sometimes gives me that penetrates to the heart. But he didn't pursue the point. "That Mexican joint on Market where we ate last week. That'll be a safe place. Everybody's always happy there."

"Sounds good." He gave me directions. I got back on the phone.

"Okay, mom, I know a place. I'll be at the corner of Fell Street and Market. Can you find that?"

"Sure, honey. I'll meet you there in about five minutes."

She pulled up in the same powder-blue Volkswagen Bug I remembered, dingy with splatter and dust from the road. The dent on the fender had rusted clean through. She waved from the car. I waved back.

She pulled over, got out, gave me a stiff hug. I hugged her back harder than I wanted to. Then she quickly said, "Let's go, honey, I have to be at the convention center by ten."

I tried to open the passenger door but the handle flopped loose in my hand. "Sorry, Davy," she blurted, "that door handle broke last week. You'll have to climb in through the driver's side here." As I clambered over the parking brake and wrestled myself into the seat, I saw that the inside door handle was missing. So was the window crank.

Off we went. "Head down Market Street six blocks," I directed, "then hang a right."

"Okay, sweetie." She began chattering away. It's been so long since I've seen you. The seminar is going to be fascinating. Psychologists from all over the country are coming. What have you been up to? It sure was a long drive from Pennsylvania. Five days. But I liked the hotel in Kansas. They don't even lock their doors there! Did you know that? They're such simple, trusting folks. I wish everybody was like that. How have you been?

She yakked right on past Sixth Street.

"Mom? You missed the turn back there." I tried to get my bearings. "I guess take the next right and we can circle around again."

"Alright, honey." She turned right on Fifth but then yakked her way right past Mission and then Howard.

"Mom!" I cried. "You missed both those turns! So, take a right at Folsom. No, doggone it, this is one-way. Take the next right, then."

But she didn't seem to be paying attention. Before I knew it the little tin can car was trapped on the onramp to the Bay Bridge.

"What's happening, mom?" I demanded.

"Oh, I'm sorry, Davy, I guess I'm kind of scattered, aren't I?"

"Well, it's alright, I guess. I think there's a turnaround at Treasure Island."

"Okay," she said.

She drove right past it.

I started to panic. I glanced over and saw that her face had slammed shut. Jaw rigid, mouth pinched, eyes hard, knuckles tight on the wheel.

"Mom," I asked quietly, "what's going on?"

Her mouth pried open to grit, "I'm driving back to Pennsylvania and I'm taking you with me. I'm going to get you straight. I know you've been on drugs." she said. "And I'm not stopping until we get there. You will have to kill me if you want to get out of this car."

No blue Volkswagen Beetle cracked open on the pavement that day. Two bloodied and mangled bodies, one blond male aged twenty-two, one white-haired female age approximately forty-eight, were not discovered by the California Highway Patrol in a tangle of bent steel and broken glass. No passenger hurled himself through a driver's window in a suicidal dive for freedom. No vehicle operator on the eastbound lane of I-80 at 9:32 AM Pacific Standard Time under a clear bright cloudless sky violently lost her life along with that of her unwilling offspring during the course of their travels.

Why was that? What allowed me over the next hour to seal inside my body such thunderous electric rage? When I recall that singular moment, it is that which truly frightens me.

Somehow I convinced her that no I am not a drug-mad maniac and no I will not kill you and yes I will go back to the state of Pennsylvania with you and yes I will not make any fuss bother or trouble on the way.

Perhaps a lifetime of containing my heart hidden behind walls of denial prepared me for the self-betrayal. Of the five days and nights of hot dusty road, greasy food, and dark, dingy motels that it took us to get to Bethel Park, I have little memory. Sometime after we arrived, Mom and Dad judged me sane and worthy and sentenced me to my former life. They bought me a bus ticket to California.

I walked to our apartment from the Greyhound station, climbed the stairs, knocked on the door. When Jon answered, his eyes flashed open, jaw dropped.

"Houghnh!" he cried. "My God! Where have you been? I'm so glad to see you!" His arms opened and I collapsed into them. "What happened? I've been going crazy! I had no idea where you went. You just disappeared."

"God, I've missed you too!"

We stood hugging for a long moment. Then he said, "Come on in. Tell me all about it."

"Do something for me first, Jon."

"What's that?"

"Can you put some Van Morrison on the turntable?"

"Sure. Which album?"

"The one where he does 'Motherless Child'."

"You bet, Ducks."

Family Ghost

Rattling in closets, spooking the guests,
moaning in frightening tongues,
tipping chairs, gutting candles,
haunting the graves of the dusty dead
or hiding in the dark of the family crypt,
this is my work.
After a busy day, the family gathers for dinner.
I am summoned to appear.
Here I am fully visible, the undead sitting at table.

I live in a room in your typical neighborhood,
a house with a roof and a kitchen with knives and
two point three dogs and a side yard laced with
dead buckets and rakes and the house floats
on the surging wave of a maddening crimson tide.
This is the place where I'm said to be loved.
I have no skin, no borders, no boundaries,
a thing so clear you can't see me,
made of what leaks from the corners of eyes.

I make the best guardian of family secrets
for everything below the slits in my bedsheet
has gone numb.
But do not imagine that a ghost like me
even though invisible to you
does not howl in anguished agony
with every cruel or careless thing you do.

43

Ashamed of my ghostliness,
absorbing disgust only I can feel,
I take on the disowned parts of others
like used rags I find on the road.
I don suits of armor, try on bright frilly dresses,
step into a pair of rough coveralls, whatever I find
discarded I make my own. I feel at home there,
folding the mix into a personal myth.

You try to pin me to statements or
find a suitable diagnosis or
God forbid! help. But you cannot.
Only I can.
I cannot.
I have no cures, no potions, no nostrums,
only legs to walk away
and arms to slap out in blind fury
and a belly to churn and to hurl
and a hurricane inside of my head.
I have all manner of tricks like
the squid with his ink
or the skunk with his stink
or the possum with his playing dead.
But I have no analgesics to soothe the pain or
to make my exquisite love of the pain disappear.
Where I live, love and pain are one.

Don't try to save me or solve me.
I'm not a poor wretch or a puzzle.
I'm a phantom whose curse is two eyes
which have come to perceive
what is hidden from view.

Come sit with me.
I know this is something you loathe to do
for it merely reminds you how
this could have happened to you.
Still, come sit. Here. Please. Sit and pretend you care.
I love above all tender caring.
I'm a sucker for tender caring.

Come live in the land of your dark side.
Sit here in the midst of the country you made.
Take in the view of what it is like to be me,
the thing that so often interferes
with the beautiful life of you—
you who've avoided the madness,
you who have learned to swallow
the sword of truth just gingerly enough
to prevent it from breaking your skin.
I wasn't so lucky, sensitive thing, me,
for I am the one who grew up in the dark,
the shadow you will not let in.

48

Narcissus

Verse I

I was born blind for my eyes were closed for all the crying
  It hurt when my body uncurled
When I opened wide, oh my, oh my, I started sighing
  In wonder at the wonder of the world
    Oh-my-oh!
My mother's eyes were the mirror to the essence my heart
  But her glass had long ago shattered
So I broke myself into a thousand pieces then they drifted apart
  And soon enough became scattered
    Oh-my-oh!
I'm a grown up now, I guess you could say
But that's not how I feel today
I wish my heart were as innocent as child's play

Verse II

So I built my castles tall then I filled up every room with little trinkets
  They blew away in windy weather
I made a lot of friends but when they said 'David, I like you!'
  I blew away like a feather
    Oh-my-oh!
Now I sit alone in my hollow room living on nothing
  That's because nothing fills me up
You can give me all the love in the world, it'll never be enough
  To fill my bottomless cup
    Oh-my-oh!

But the night must surrender to the day
And the light will reveal a way
To stitch my wound so I can finally say

Chorus 1
I'm not afraid anymore, or running anymore,
    Or moving away from the pain
Or messing with myself, second guessing myself,
    Running naked under the rain
I don't have to play dead any more
    I don't have to pretend
That was my house, it'll never be my home again

Verse III
Have you heard about Narcissus, how he gazed down deep into the water,
    Fell in love with his reflection?
"I must have her!" he cried, and he searched for a lifetime
    In every other direction
        Oh-my-oh!
Broke his back moving mountains and diving down dead-end alleys
    I guess you know how the story ended
He finally realized that he himself was his beloved
    And that's how his heart was mended
        Oh-my-oh!

That was when he found a best friend
Loyal from beginning to end
He got the message that his body had been trying to send

Chorus II
I'm not alone anymore, on my own anymore
   I've found someone to love
Not the one I seemed to know in the water down below
   But the one waiting here up above
I'll never have to go back there now
   Because I'll never forget where we've been
That was my house, it'll never be my home again
      Oh-my-oh!
never be my home again
      Oh-my-oh!
never be my home again!

Narcissus

Words and Music ~ David Bayard

August 2021

2

August 2021

54

3

August 2021

Broken Folks

You'll see them living under trees,
 in dead cars by freeways,
  at the back of dead parking lots in urban corners,
shuffling down sidewalks, spilling half-out
 the rude doors of asylums and
even from a distance you know something's different.
 Maybe they're obvious, arms akimbo, legs dancing in
  odd lunar motions or maybe an inner break,
 invisible hairline fracture of bone.
You feel pity at first then a door closes.
You sidle by guilty or maybe jealous of how well
 they hold pain. You try to imagine what is beyond
your experience, but not stand so close it rubs off on you.
 There but for the grace, you mumble as prayer
for something so far outside of your everywhere.

As I watch the broken from distance
 something inside splits apart.
Now I can see I am just like them.

I have been broken too

  long ago learned the art of painting on skin

    depictions of wholeness which

      overlay heartache within.

Only the broken watching can see

  the break which is hidden to me.

Only those born with eyes calibrated to pain

    can tell when somebody else

  falls to the truth of their bodies again.

My body is two and they're fighting,

  one broken one whole, the whole one says 'fix yourself!'

    broken says 'screw you, go break yourself!'

Where can we meet without combat

  where we're not further broken but

    knit together like loving wool scarves?

Where neither one starves or is shunned

  or denied their ticket to heaven?

We are all broken fragments of soul

  not destined in life to mend whole.

Meantime we suffer in different degrees,

  all of our pillows in vain.

Down comes the rain on the just and the unjust,
  everyone living together, the glorious mud and the dust,
    wholly alive till we're broken.
Walking on streets in the rain like a movie
  showing to an empty house,
    moving in jerky spasmodic rhythms of pain
  till all that we are is a grace,
    a movement through time and through space
  that makes of our suffering worthwhile.
Here in the land which is ours alone,
  the shore of the endless ocean of wholeness,
    we stand finally solid, awaiting the
  tide.

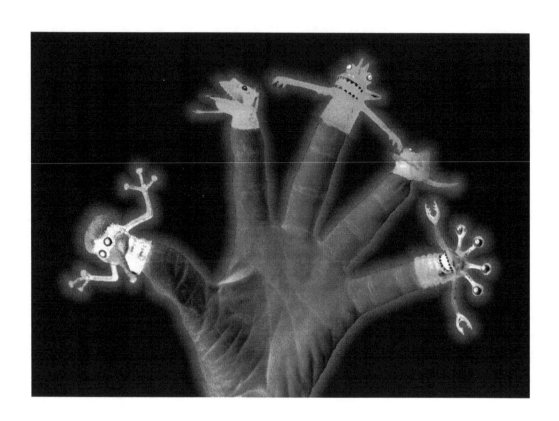

When Monsters Come

When monsters come from under bed

deep inside a turgid dream

I run I flee my feet in dark tar pumping

arms grasp at grasses pull the useless body

flail useless legs

scissor teeth behind me clacking

fiery breath upon my neck hair burning

heart implodes I am unbreathing eyes are blind

cannot turn around cannot move

black blood like gasoline flashes off my body

I am trapped in amber waiting for

what

never comes

Running there so steeped in red,
what turns your body toward betrayal?
What seizes on your tossing limbs with all its
paralyzing venom, readies you for sacrifice?
In this way you fulfill the fiendish plans,

abandon yourself to agree with the

beast that you deserve death.

Stop your running, just you

stop!

Now I turn fully about,

present my true self to the mirror.

They're surprised! Their fierce expressions dissolve.

My resolve has unmasked them.

They are embarrassed, bewildered,

they appear lost, so lonely, shuffling about in confusion.

Sweetly I reach out, caress their rough spiny faces,

watch them soften. I hold them in close embrace.

I feel their hunger for my form, my meanings,

their lust for my dark desires.

They have been chasing me in order

to find their meaning

for they are born of me.

I befriend them. Their bloodlust is nothing more

than the terror inside my heartbeat.

You, my totems, my allies, my secret battalion,
I take you out when I need fierce protection,
we go to the deli for rye bread sandwiches
and glasses of sweet lemonade.
You accompany me on hazardous duties and trials.
Time and time and time you boost my heels
to the sills of soot-blackened doorways
where we stand naked before the shadow of ourselves
and launch into the great unknown,
leap to the world immortal.

The author in the demilitarized zone, South Korea, in the
summer of 1968

We Loves Us Some War

We love our wars as we love our lovers.
We enjoy the thumping
chopper crunch of bones in air
beating down the sky.
Whump! Whump! Whump! they go
in such a satisfying mirage of eros.
There is a grace in that bloody embrace
even as it sickens, as if we'd
been caught masturbating. We can't look away.
It is a fun, shooting, spurting spree with a detachment
that tricks us into watching it all
happen to someone else.
We ruin ourselves expressing the truth
that we hate ourselves more
than any enemy we encounter.

Count down, ten to one, explode the
munition of mutiny, expressly forbidden by God.
If we had but known!
Damn, why didn't you tell us?
We love war's bold disregard for all:

for morality, decency, humanity,
though not, ironically, for law,
where war is lovingly codified.

But maybe we'll survive, we say.
This is the hope that keeps war in our clutch,
the downward spiral grip, the
death's-head grin as we follow our hand into the
shredder, we think to ourselves,
maybe we will win.

Or maybe we say to our created enemy *you can't push us around*
or *you pushed us to it* as we push ourselves into meaningless
carnage or victory like shards of glass in the mouth or
losing like shards in the belly.

No one goes to war to die, says the General.
They go to war to live. Some just die in the process.
We love to live, we live to lose, we hate to die
and a part of us dies in the process.
Losing and loving are but one letter apart.
We are saints and sinners who
lie to our lovers and hearts.

The Rape of My Story

I want to write this as someone else's poem.
This is not me. I am not here.

I try to stand on top of the pain to
rise above but it grows up through
the soles of my feet.

I speak of the invisible I would rather die than see
a vicious beast upon my throne who
wears my robes, busy lifting my ID
who passes through my skin at will
while disguising deep disgust about my body.
I speak of mother mine.
There, I said it.

Wait,   take it back,

                        start the poem over
   before the punishment grows inside me yet again.

                        [In a Dream] I am running from the bad thing
                                    into an abyss, a basement,
                              down dark dusty stairs reeking,
                           past the taxidermy statues of my body.
                     I come to the bottom, the stairway disappears.

I look around in panic as the walls shrink in.
I open all the windows of my eyes
I believe I see a lonely hole within my heart
when I look it closes
[I awaken]

I speak of scores of years it took to learn
that I sprang from loins purloined
of a girl whose spirit too was shattered.
I was blinded by a rape that felt
As light as whispered daisies.
Now I'll do this poem how I want to.
Her disgust within my body cannot break it.

I've been gaslit by a master,
prepared, as it were, familiar,
so that later when the real rape happened
I was too inured to see it for the
slippery violation that it was
a trick
disguising depredation as selflessness
a saving of the soul, unrecognized even by the rapist
thereby sliding by the normal gateways
which innocents must close to save their souls
from falling into grief's yawning chasm.

I'm saying I'm an ocean that I
gasp in like I'm drowning.

I'm saying when I pull the skin off near my belly button
I see maggots of self-loathing writhing there.
I'm saying that I see how I swallow any love that I am offered
how I spit up all I swallow
how I gobble up the world yet I'm still crying empty
how I'm crying, crying, crying, being hollow

                    In a dream: my mouth is filled with cotton
                              filled with broken glass and
                    strips of carpet. I cannot seem to spit them out,
          no water, I am running seeking water, seeking running water,
                    pulling chunk and shards out with my fingers,
                              hoping no one sees me
                    but the putrid mass of my disgust
                    grows back like fungus, tongue is tied
                    with hopeless task of spitting
                              [I awaken]

how I could not be trusted with my life,
how it was her job to live it for me, live it through me,
how she could not see my boundaries
how she had no borders of her own,
how my skin erupts in lava flows,
how there is a boil on my back larger,
more important than a house fire

          In a dream: I run along the hard steel tracks, back bent,

arms wrapped round my precious parcel
as the city burns, dark horizon black in sooty smoke.
I hold the child tightly as a football I must carry down the field of fire.
I must protect the child.
I am running from the future to the past
repairing broken dreams alone
with the bundle at my bosom
[I wake up inside the dream]

A trick of light spilling from the fractures of my heart
plays upon my open eyes.
I know enough to raise my hands. They are blue-white fire.
I look up to find myself and child alone.
The two of us are one,
on our own,
Loving one another as we did
long ago in hidden caverns by the sea
within our safe abode, pulling one another's tides
like ancient secrets out across the endless shore.

I could never speak of this for language was verboten
yet I now have spoken
I will mend the places where I'm broken
I will grow a summer flower from my mouth
nourished by the flow of deeper rivers.

Prometheus

Sit here with me and I shall sing a saga true and bold
A tale of gods and mortal heroes longing to be told
Which future stale museum oils do not truly tell.
Hear me now for memory serves me well.

Such chaos in the agony of the groaning earth!
A thousand bloody struggles in the fire of her birth
Giants fought for primacy within the empty void.
All but mighty Zeus were soon destroyed.

Though he bested every foe he did not win alone
For he enlisted anyone whose loyalty was shown.
The fiercest of his allies and defenders came to be
Prometheus, the Titan that is me.

Zeus soon forgot that I had helped defeat his foes.
Time folded into time till the dawn of man arose.
I am also mortal thus was moved to see their plight
Beings born of darkness, made of light.

Though a mortal Titan I am closer to a god,
Privy to the magic which Olympus long outlawed.
While the race of man cowered naked in the rain
I thought of clever ways to ease their pain.

I taught them many simple tricks to even up the odds,
I mirrored their true nature thus I showed them they were gods.
I shared the vital secret that all living things are one,
That everything descended from the sun.

I brought no gift to humankind for who can steal fire?
Imagination was the spark I struck to lift them higher.
I held the bold ideas which the gods had shared with me
Before the lifted eyes of man to see.

From this arose the punishment for deeds I could not hide,
My gifts to man the one thing jealous Zeus could not abide.
He banished me from heaven out onto the ocean's swell
To suffer through a special kind of hell.

Hermes fetched me, brought me here, chained me to this stone.

His tender heart cracked open once he saw me here alone.

Before he left, he placed within my hand the precious key.

I flung it out into the endless sea.

The winged god meant well in his offered mercy mild

But Zeus is the god to whom I must be reconciled.

This I cannot do until I see his heart has healed

And the love underlying is revealed.

For I cannot in conscience save but myself alone

Until toward all creatures be that mercy shown.

Thus the fishes of the sea and the birds that course the sky

Shall find the key more useful than would I.

I yearned for a father who was patient, kind and wise

Whose vision would display to me the wonder of the skies,

A mother who would cradle me with whispered words of love

Gentle as the cooing of a dove.

Zeus was not my father but as any father might
He taught me by example how to live in truth and light.
But god though he may be, he is as flawed as any man.
He betrayed me just as any father can.

I suffered from his constant pecking at my self-regard,
His stinging thoughtless insults, his fury cruel and hard,
His blindness to my virtues, this has all converged in me,
Lonely Titan chained to stone upon the sea.

And Hera was no mother as I needed her to be.
Her vain shallow selfishness mattered more than me.
Her jealousy of any who would not proclaim her fair
With her frilly garments and her hair.

As long as they are blind to me then I will not be moved.
I pity them the more, for I fear it may be proved
Their banishment within their self-made cage shall come to be
Far worse than any punishment of me.

Zeus and Hera's reign brought both glory and upheaval.

Though gods they are an all-too-human mix of good and evil.

To them forgiveness flows thus abundantly from me

For from this new perspective I now see.

Eagles daily rend my flesh which nightly is renewed

Or so the ancient tale goes, but it was misconstrued.

Great raptors seldom venture this far out to sea.

The only bird of prey lives in me.

I did not choose my gods, those who've betrayed my faith.

But I can choose to waste myself into a wretched wraith.

Bone to dust, blood to brine, leaving only heart

This is my sole remaining art.

I shall not dissolve from the form I took on Earth

For my soul to that larger soul has been given birth

The source of all that is, a firmament that sings

Of endless love for all living things.

My body is a candle flame with which I light the world.

Unchained my spirit rises, my love at last unfurled.

If in future this bright fire persists in burning hot

Then fate of wick and wax matters not.

I become the ocean deep whose spirit sings with whales.

My breath shall feed the ceaseless wind in breezes as in gales.

My tears shall fall from heaven to become the lightning rain

Bringing forth on earth new life again.

My gentle voice shall beckon you from every hill and hollow.

So let your throat open wide, cry 'Follow! Follow! Follow!'

For thus my life has written vivid in a hand so fair

My epitaph upon the rising air.

— For Stephan

Medusa

Once I lived a maiden fair, pure in innocence
   In the spring of life's beginning age
My future days a book which I stood ready to unfold
   Trembling there upon the open page

O how I wish I could relive those golden days
   When all the world was just as it should be
All the wild grasses singing bright hallelujahs
   But alas is it no longer so with me

For I was far too comely for Poseidon to resist
   My ripeness did inflame his wild lust
His darker nature took its course in raw and naked plunder
   The god despoiled my innocence and trust

His vile rape burst me open, sundered me in two
  A part of me then shriveled up and died
In its place you arose, the shadow of myself
  While I hid in fear deep inside

How constant, how relentless is this sense of not belonging!
  Of emptiness, self-loathing and despair
With these writhing monsters I am singularly cursed
  A thousand tangled serpents in my hair

I speak to you, my other half. We are so alone
  For the tender bridge between us has been broken
Your countenance so hideous is all the world sees
  When they hear me, it is you who have spoken

  I have nothing left to offer you but bitterness and spite
    My bile throws up boils on your face
  Pray thee strike me down now, it is our only hope
    To end the mutual misery of this place

Only I can heal the hateful thing we have become
  I alone can crack this brittle shell
Only I can mend the tear that keeps us far apart
  Only I can lift us up from hell

> *Find your sword of truth then, hold it firm and steady*
>   *Learn the subtle arts to wield it well*
>   *Cut through every web of fear that has been woven*
>   *We may yet survive, who can tell*

I find a sheet of crystal glass then silver it to see
  The single spirit that we truly are
Behold the creature we've become since violation's curse
  How the wound became an ugly scar

In its bright reflection I see I am doubly cursed
  But I see a path to heal the soul
My psyche from my body has been torn away and broken
  Now I hold the power to make us whole

Then pray step you boldly now into my monster's lair

Keep your shield before you and be bold

I will try to turn your sword with endless feints and tricks

Thrashing, boiling, work to loose your hold

Step by lonely step I steal across the endless floor

Walking backward, looking in the mirror

You may even welcome what is coming, my sweet half,

The demise of your cruelly long career

Then, sweet half, turn your simple pain into a weapon

Smite this belly full of broken bones

My dying will release the ancient curse of our betrayal

Make us whole now. Take me as your own

I may spend a lifetime working closer to the beast

My bright resolve will often turn to lead

But one day a wondrous cry will burst out from my throat:

"Off with the dreaded Gorgon's head!"

Rising

To those who endeavor to heal the Psyche

Such brave and magnificent birds!

Phoenixes willing to leap into flames

Saving souls using nothing but words.

"You're crazy!" she screamed. "You are just plain crazy! You need therapy! I don't, I've got it together, but boy, you sure do! What's your problem?"

This was when I knew it was over between us.

We'd been together for four years. All we did was scream and curse and argue. I couldn't live like this anymore.

I didn't respond. Too stopped up with rage. I didn't follow Pat back home, either, after she stomped off. Instead, I wandered over to the derelict carriage house on Warwick my boss said I could use if I needed. It didn't have heat, gas, or walls. But, hey, it had electricity and a roof. That's all I needed. I had the skills to fix it up. I spent the rest of the day looking the place over, getting ready.

That night I finally went back to the apartment, my mind reliving everything that had happened that day. I didn't tell Pat my plans. I didn't say much all night, in fact, just grunted a few words over dinner and went straight to bed.

When I thought about what she'd said that day, though, I realized that she was half right. The part about her not needing therapy was a total crock. But as for me?

She was right on. I needed help.

I opened the office door to find my new client in the waiting room. He sat under the floor lamp, rooted to the curved-back chair, a notebook on his knees which jiggled to the rhythm of his scribbling. His face was hidden under a thicket of curly blond hair, ringlets fluttering in the light's amber glow. His worn T-shirt and paint-spattered jeans were festooned with sawdust and wood shavings. The air smelled of pine.

"David?" I asked.

He looked up. A pair of crystal-blue eyes furtively met mine. As he hurriedly closed the notebook, his pen clattered to the floor. He reached for it, fumbled it into his pocket.

"Yes?"

"I'm Guideone. Pleased to meet you. Would you like to come into my office?" He rose in the gangly, awkward, yet somehow graceful way a stork might move. He followed me into the room.

Once inside, I motioned him to the big armchair. He sat at first hesitantly, then settled in and looked around the room.

"I like your garden," he said, once his gaze reached the front window. "I checked it out when I came in."

"Thanks. Do you garden?"

"No, but I've been thinking about it. I have a place now with a back yard. Mostly overgrown with weeds, though. But I like digging in dirt."

I nodded. "I see. Well, David," I began, "when we spoke over the phone, you mentioned some issues you're having your girlfriend. Tell me about that."

"Yeah...well," he said, eyes fixed on at my shoes, "I've broken up with her since then, so it's a moot point, but I guess that's why I'm here. I left her, then came back again, a couple times, actually. I think this time it's for good. But, you know, I realized I don't want to keep repeating the same mistakes over and over. With her, or anybody."

"Does it feel like that's what you've been doing?"

"Yeah. And I want to get a handle on that."

"So, tell me about your relationship."

They met in San Francisco, moved in together. Sometime later she decided they would homestead at a hippie commune in the Ozark woods. Did he want to come? Yes. He built a tiny cabin out of scrap lumber in the bed of an old Dodge pickup. They loaded the truck and a blue Volkswagen van with all their belongings and headed east to Missouri.

Spent most of a year tucked into deep woods, a big adventure in the frigid Midwestern winter. But as spring came and faded into summer, they grew increasing unhappy together. He left and headed to Colorado to cut timber in the mountains.

Meantime the commune had fallen apart. Pat made her way to Kansas City, the nearest big town, and found a cheap roach-infested apartment overlooking Gilham Park. David, lonely for her, returned from Colorado. But they soon became miserable again. He decided to finally leave. He found a gutted, abandoned house, bought it, began fixing it up to live in.

I paused a moment to digest his story. "That's quite a tale," I allowed. "I'm glad you had the courage to seek help." "I won't charge you for this session. You can decide if this feels like a good fit and if you'd like to continue to work with me."

"That sounds good," he returned. "I was in therapy when I was a kid, long time ago."

"So you know a little bit about the process. Tell me about your childhood. What was it like for you growing up?"

He sighed at the ceiling fan. "I think I was pretty happy as a child. I remember our family went camping in the mountains a lot in the Pennsylvania woods. Hiking and stuff. I think that's where I got my love of nature. And I remember reading books with my mom. Lying on their big bed in front of this huge bookshelf and just dreaming. That was one of my favorite things.

"She's a psychologist. We'd talk about writing, and it was sort of an adventure. My dad's a nuclear physicist. He worked on the Nautilus submarine, you know, the first nuclear-powered vessel. I picked up a love of science from him. I was into astronomy big-time, had a telescope and all. And chemistry and math."

"So, you have mostly happy memories?" I asked.

"Well, as a young kid, yeah. But I got really depressed when I was about fourteen or so. That was a hard time for me."

"I see." I paused for a moment to check in with myself. I wasn't breathing, my stomach felt tight, and I desperately wanted to bolt out the door.

"David," I continued, "let's try something. Before we go any further, right now I'm curious what it feels like being in your body."

He looked puzzled. "What do you mean? In my body?"

"Yes. If you would please, just relax, take a deep breath, and see if you can tell what's going on inside, how you're feeling."

"Okay," he said. He took a shallow breath, leaned back. After a moment, "I feel—I don't know what I feel. It's just my body, I guess, right?"

"Just tell me the first thing you're aware of, then."

Sigh. "Well, my belly feels kind of tight," he said.

"Okay. What else?"

A deeper sigh. His eyes closed. "I guess I feel sort of tight all over. Like I'm afraid to breathe."

"I hear you. Anything else?"

"Well," he said hesitantly, "this might sound weird, but I feel like I just want to get out of here. I know I asked to see you and all, but right now I just want to run away."

"That doesn't seem at all weird to me. This is a scary thing to do, opening yourself up in front of a total stranger. I don't blame you.

"And just so you know, you can bolt out the door anytime you like. I certainly won't stop you. But I do encourage you to stay with that feeling of wanting to run. Stay with what it feels like, without having to act upon it."

I paused. "You're safe here, David."

It was these last words set me crying. Not because I felt safe now, though for some reason I did. But because I realized there had never been a place in the real world where I felt truly safe. I suddenly recalled my special space from long ago, with the jiggling stars and the purple parakeets. I closed my eyes.

It was as if that space had suddenly blossomed inside the room. Salty tears began stinging their way down my cheeks.

I expected Guidone to interrupt, shush me, tell me not to cry.

Instead, "You don't have to do anything, David. I'm quite comfortable sitting here with you. I'm not going anywhere."

I felt my body rise and fall in a fluid tide. I felt my body! The tears are what I want, I thought. I'll just sit here and cry for all eternity if I want to. I crave this. It feels so good to let things have their way with me.

I opened my eyes to see Guidone holding out a box of tissues to me.

"Thanks," I snuffled, accepting one.

"Take the whole box, please."

Tissue in one hand, box in the other, I dabbed my eyes. "I don't know where all that came from."

"That doesn't matter. What matters is that you can let yourself have it. I think you've earned the right."

I didn't know what to say so I said nothing. And suddenly realized that didn't seem to be a problem, here inside this safe room. I felt myself expand. Every breath created more room inside.

"David, I think I can help you. But the type of therapy I practice isn't what you might call the quick fix. I believe if we don't get to the root of your unhappiness, you'll be paying me for nothing.

"It will take time to work through your deeper issues. How much, I can't say. You'll have to be willing to look at some uncomfortable truths. If I'm to help you, I need you to be in it for the long haul. Do you think you'd like to do that?"

To my surprise, I found myself excited. For the first time in a long while, I felt a sense of hope. "Yes. I'm ready," I said.

"Good. Then let's set up a session for two weeks from now and see where it leads us."

Walking back to my car past the sumptuous garden, stepping into the morning light, I carried that sense of safe harbor with me. A seed had been planted--no, I had planted a seed--which might finally have found fertile soil.

It was late November, many months later. The garden window was a winter postcard scene hazy behind a film of snow, spent bones of plants poking up through the drifts: allium on their tall stalks like fireworks frozen mid-explosion, feathery pampas grass waving in the wind, the gnarled oak tree reaching out leafless arms. David sat entranced. I waited till he was ready.

"So, I want to tell you about Carnegie Institute," he said.

"I went there after high school." He told me the story of his brief time at college, the dorm theft, the confused jumble of events in his memory.

"So that's it," he concluded. "That's when I had to go into the Army."

"It sounds like it was quite a traumatic experience for you," I said.

"Well, I hadn't thought of it as traumatic but I guess it was. I just felt bad about stealing the record player. I don't blame my parents for being mad."

I had a suddenly realization. "I think it was actually a very courageous thing to do."

He looked startled. "What do you mean?"

"We've talked about how you'd always felt inadequate around your father. Felt as if you failed to live up to his expectations. But he never told you what they were. That doesn't mean he didn't have any, he just wouldn't share them with you.

"Nevertheless, you must have sensed he wanted something for you. A hidden agenda. You had to guess what it was, then jump through all kinds of hoops to please him. And nothing you did was ever good enough. That's called a no-win situation. Tell me, did you want to be at Carnegie Institute, with an engineering major?"

He shrugged. "Not really. I thought I did at first."

"Were you doing it because you thought it was what your father would want?"

He pondered. "I hadn't thought of it that way. But I—I guess I was."

"Then once you were there, you realized it wasn't for you. Would you have been able to tell him that? To say, 'Dad, I don't want to be in this school anymore. I want to do something else.'"

"Probably not."

"That's why I'm suggesting it was a resourceful move, a clever way to get out of the situation without having to ask your dad. Does that make sense?"

"Hmm. I guess so."

"It was your only way out of an impossible pickle. You probably knew on some level that by stealing the turntable, you'd get kicked out of college and wouldn't have to do the impossible task of confronting him," I explained.

"But why courageous?"

"Because," I said, "you decided to honor yourself and your needs instead of his. You saved yourself from an unhappy life. You got what you needed for David. It was brave because to do it, you had to risk getting kicked out of college, being humiliated, having to join the army. Not to mention losing his love."

"But it screwed up my life!"

"That's right. You paid a heavy price. But the alternative would have been to deny your heart and stay on a path that wasn't what you wanted. Live the rest of your life as your father wanted without ever discovering what was right for you. I'd say you saved your life."

I paused for effect. "Let's try something. Imagine you're in your dad's workshop, the time you told him you wanted your own Chemistry lab. We'll pretend I'm your father. Go ahead and ask me for what you want."

He took a breath. "Dad, I want to put my chem lab in the basement."

"'I don't think that's a good idea, David. I'd rather you put your chem lab in my workshop.'"

"But I don't want to, dad."

"'Well, I want you to. I would rather have you set it up here. I'll even give you these four drawers to put your chemicals and equipment in. How's that?'"

"But I want my own shop, dad," he pleaded.

"'I think it would be better up here,'" I persisted.

He seemed befuddled. His eyebrows pursed. "But why

108

can't I have it downstairs? There's a nice space under the stairwell that's perfect. I already cleaned it out."

I stepped out of character. "You don't have to justify yourself to him, David. Tell him what you want."

He squared his shoulders. "I just don't want to do it, dad."

"'Well, but I think you should put the lab here.'"

"I don't care!" he shouted. "I don't care what you think! I want to put it in the basement."

"How does it feel to say that?" I asked.

"Whew! Scary as hell!" He was shaking.

"What are you scared of? What will he do?"

"He'll be mad at me."

"What would happen if he were mad?"

He shook his head, snorted, "I guess it would mean I'm a worthless piece of crap."

"Oh. So, when your father is angry, it means you're a bad person?"

"Yeah, right!"

"And we've talked about what a familiar place that is for you. How much you felt at home. How comfortable you are when you're seen as their bad little boy. And I notice something else there. You've saved him from having to feel his own feelings once again."

"How?"

"I don't know, exactly. Tell me if this feels right. He's disappointed with you, maybe, he doesn't know how to deal with his feelings, he gets upset with you but doesn't show it. Instead, he just quietly walks away. And you have no idea what he feels. But still, you read his body language. You know he's upset. It's your job to take care of him. Whatever it takes to get him to like you again. You need his affection. So to get it, you jump in and save him from having to feel his upset."

He pondered for a moment. "Oh, that sounds so right, Guidone. Like the time my mother came downstairs to tell me I'd made him cry."

"A perfect example," I seconded. "I remember that story. No one has the power to make someone else feel. When someone says, 'You made me mad,' what they're really saying is: you touched a painful place in me, and my own response was to get angry.

"You touched something in your father that brought tears. That's on him, not you. To blame his son for his own feeling was a terrible burden to place on a child. And then your mother covered for him. They double-teamed you. You

110

saved them both from having to feel. How convenient."

"Yeah," he said, "that makes such good sense. I never thought of it that way."

"Of course you didn't. You were just a child. You were entirely at their mercy. And they took advantage of that."

"But they weren't bad people," he interjected.

"No, they weren't. They were doing all they knew how to do. It doesn't matter their reasons or purpose, they betrayed your trust. A deep violation of your spirit. You were just a defenseless child."

He inhaled, sighed. "I want to sit with this for a while. It's not the image I had of them. I don't know what to believe."

This seemed to me a sensitive moment.

"I understand. I'm not asking you to believe or not to believe, just giving you another way to look at things. Trying to navigate the conflicts and impossible expectations laid on you is what I call 'crazymaking'. Whether they were aware they were doing it or not doesn't really matter.

"But let's come back to this later. Meantime I'll give you some homework: practice asking for what you want. Stand before the mirror, maybe, pretend you're talking to your parents. See how it feels. Watch what happens in your body. Your body knows. Then let's meet again in two weeks."

"Okay, I'm ready. I'll see you then."

The light spilling through the garden window was now the lime-green of spring. A tangle of flowers basked in the morning sun: purple jonquils, yellow daffodils, red begonias, the beginnings of blue salvia. David sat solidly planted in the armchair, silently contemplating the riotous profusion.

So far, we'd been focusing on his relationship with his father. The difficulties he'd experienced as a child are common to most men: the struggle to form a separate identity in the face of a fathers' unspoken and often contradictory demands. But with David, I was beginning to sense there was something more to the puzzle, something I had been missing.

Or rather, someone.

I began the session, "So is there anything you'd like to work on today?"

He looked at me, sighed, leaned back into the armchair. His gaze returned to the garden window. "Yes," he began, "there's this one thing that's bothering me. It's about a book my mom sent me."

"Yes?"

"Well," he began, "a few weeks ago she sent me a book that she and my dad wrote. It's like a guide for parents about how to deal with their acting-up teenagers, kids who are stealing, lying, getting in trouble, that sort of thing."

"So, what about it bothered you?"

"Well, so, I read it, and in one of the chapters my mother used me as an example of an acting-up teenager. Told a story about me. I had borrowed her Volkswagen bug for a trip to Boston. The first time I ever took a on my own. I was going there to look at a college. Anyway, I forgot to put oil in the engine and it burned up on the way back to Pittsburgh. They had to have it towed back. She was really mad."

"How old were you?"

"Seventeen, I guess. The summer after I graduated high school."

"Had she told you to add oil to the engine?"

"She probably had, but to be honest I don't remember," he confessed.

"And you're thirty-one now. The first thing that strikes me is not the burned-up engine or whether she told you to change the oil or not, but the fact that now, years later, they use you in a book as an example of an acting-up child. Did they ever ask your permission?"

"No."

"Did your mother even mention the fact that you were in the book?"

"No. She just sent a note that said they were proud of having written it and wanted me to have a copy."

"Wow. So, you first learned about your cameo as a 'bad' child when you read the book?"

"Yup."

"How did that feel?"

He considered that for a long moment. "I'll tell you, Guidone, I think I was pretty angry."

"I'll bet you were! If it helps to know, I would be absolutely livid if someone did that to me."

He gave a self-conscious laugh. "Yeah, I was."

"I don't blame you. Did you tell them how you felt?" I asked.

"I haven't had any contact with them since the Army. At least not much. So, no. This sort of came out of the blue."

I thought about this for good while. Then, "David, you told me of other incidents that strike me as very similar. The time she kept you in a broom closet eight hours a day for a month to do homework for a college you didn't want to attend. And the time she kidnapped you from San Francisco and drove to Pennsylvania to 'straighten you out,' as you put it. She asserts the right to take charge of your life any time she likes.

"So, let's work with this. We'll start with the acting-up teenager book." I tossed a pillow to him. "This is mom. You just read her book and now you're talking to her. What do you want to say to her?"

He held the pillow at arm's length as if holding a live rattlesnake. His eyes closed, opened, then, "I don't want to say anything. I just want to strangle her."

"Why don't you?"

"I feel stuck. It feels like I hold myself tight against her." He winced. "Wow, yeah. I can see her coming and I feel paralyzed. My belly tightens up and I can't move."

"Don't go away. Stay here," I insisted. "This is what it felt like to be little David. But you're safe now. She can't get to you." He rocked back and forth in the chair, clutching the mom pillow. "Just let yourself have this. As a child, you had to abandon yourself to keep her around. You had to go numb. You don't have to do that anymore. You can have this feeling now. I'm right here. Keep breathing. What do you want from her right now?"

His hands tightened around the pillow's throat. "I'm not letting you in anymore!" he cried. Then he winced and pulled his face away.

"No, don't go away. Tell her how you feel."

"I want to smash your face!" he screamed.

"Go ahead."

I pummeled that stupid pillow mercilessly. It jumped and twitched madly with each blow. That wasn't enough. I twisted her stupid face in my hands, my teeth grinding. I smashed her down in a frenzy of anger, again and again and again.

I don't know how long I slammed my precious oh-so-fragile mother, my wonderful caring and loving mother, down onto the hot anvil of my knees. I gave myself over to bottomless rage, letting delicious vengeance overtake me.

Eventually I closed my eyes and collapsed back into the soft comfort of the armchair, spent. After what seemed like hours, I awoke to the familiar room. Guidone sat watching with quiet attentive presence.

"How do you feel?" floated softly in the air.

I had to work for an answer, surprised to hear myself say, "It felt wrong. I don't know what I mean—I mean, it felt awful. Now I feel ashamed of what I just did. Wow. Like I betrayed her." I began breathing hard.

"I'm not surprised. You were never allowed to have these feelings. Your mother would have cut you off from all love, af-

fection, attention. Abandoned you, emotionally if not physically. You could never afford to let that happen.

"David, you were a victim of abuse."

My mind reeled. "But...but Guidone," I protested, "she never
ever hit me or anything. Neither of them did. What do you mean,
abuse?"

"No, she didn't physically hurt you. Your parents were much
too nice for that. What they did, specifically what she did,
was much worse. She didn't respect your boundaries. She didn't
allow you to be a separate person. She invaded your privacy any
time she felt like it and you were totally helpless. Her viola-
tions became the normal thing. That is abuse. But no wonder you
didn't recognize it as such.

"David, I've worked with patients who've suffered physical
abuse as children. Beatings, incest, rape, torture, you name it.
These all inflict deep emotional trauma. I've seen the effects.
And I see the same things going on with you. But, see, there's
nothing I can point to and say, 'Look, David! Look! Here's the
evidence! These broken bones, these cigarette burns on your
arm, these lash marks on your back. They prove you were abused!'

"With emotional abuse, the marks are invisible, but the wounds
are there just the same. That's why I say it's worse. If there
were obvious signs, if you had traumatic memories, it might be
easier for you to recognize. Easier for us to work with. But
because it all happened under the radar, you have no way to ex-

plain or understand or process your unhappiness. I think of it as invisible trauma."

"I want to believe that," I ventured.

"What gets in the way of that?"

I sat with that question for a moment. "It feels like I'm being disloyal to her," I concluded.

"How convenient for her. In a test of loyalty between you and her, she always wins. She thought of it as her job to live your life for you."

What snapped immediately into my memory were the many blatant examples of that in my life. Not just the ones Guidone had mentioned, or the teenager book, but all the many different ways she would traipse across the border of my skin, come right in and do exactly as she pleased.

Suddenly came the memory of the dream from so long ago, guarding the Russian sector against her intrusion. Knowing I should shoot but unable to move. How had this become just the normal way of life for me? Why had I not recognized any of this?

I sat in silence for a long time, letting this revelation filter down to my bones. I felt Guidone's presence. For once, somebody who was totally on my side. I understood that now.

I resisted the urge for further speech. I sighed deeply and said, "I feel finished for today."

"Let's end here then, David. I agree, this has been a powerful session."

"Yeah, for sure. Thank you, Guidone."

"You don't need to thank me. It's my job to model what good support, good parental love, looks like. And unlike with your mother, you don't have to do anything to earn it."

I didn't know what to say.

But a little imp inside me did. "Except to pay you," I said.

We both erupted in laughter. "Yes, that's true!" Guidone allowed. "And very funny!"

"I know," I snickered. "It's been a long time since I made a joke. I believe I'm getting my sense of humor back."

David gazes out the window, where the humid heat of August is a weighted blanket on the garden as it pants in the hot sun. We've watched the scene evolve together over the time we've been working together. It has become the way he begins each session.

"Some of your flowers are gone now, I just realized. And new ones I haven't seen before," he said. "It's been what, almost four years now I've been seeing you?"

"Something like that," I agreed.

"It feels like this has saved my life."

"I'm glad to hear that. But we're not done yet. So, David," I began, "what would you like to work on today?"

He took a breath. "I'd like to talk about Bobbie."

"Your girlfriend? What's going on?"

"Well, I feel really helpless with her. I always wind up feeling like I'm doing something wrong. She can be kind of harsh sometimes."

"Give me an example."

"Well, we were at a juice bar getting drinks and the waitress just wasn't getting what Bobbie was saying. She kept repeating 'no ice, no ice' and the waitress just wasn't hearing her. She served up a drink, put ice in it and handed it over to Bobbie, who just dumps the whole thing back into the ice bin, drops the cup in a real cold way, and walks out the door.

"I was floored. I'm left standing there with the poor woman looking stunned and I have no idea what to do. I eventually caught up with Bobbie. She didn't say anything, and I didn't either. But I was mad the whole time."

"Why didn't you speak up?"

He twisted in the chair. "I guess I didn't want to upset

her."

"What were you afraid would happen if you told her how you felt?"

"I don't know, I just didn't want to bring it up. It was easier to let it slide. She's like, I'm...well, being with her is sometimes like holding a live grenade."

"How does your body feel right now as you're telling me this?"

He closed his eyes, sank into the chair. "Like I'm closed in. Strapped to a gurney or something. I'm not supposed to move. Stuck."

"That sounds familiar, doesn't it?"

A snort, "Yeah. Right. Mom again."

"It's the only way you know how to relate to people. A healthy relationship was never modeled for you."

"Can't seem to get away from her, can I?"

He was silent for a spell. Then, "I guess there's another thing." He looked at me sheepishly. "We don't make love very much anymore. She's never in the mood. And I'm afraid to ask."

"Have you discussed this with her?"

"A couple times. But I get all bolluxed up in my head

and I can't tell what's going on. It feels like work. I can't even reach out to touch her without it feeling like I'm doing something wrong."

"Sex is always part of the larger picture of relationships. You're afraid to broach any subject with Bobbie, and sex is of course particularly sensitive. So, let's see how it feels to ask her for something, anything. What's it like to have your own needs and desires when you're with her? Pretend she's sitting there," I said, pointing to the empty chair. "Ask her for what you want. Tell her how you feel."

He looked at "Bobbie" in the chair. "Okay, then. 'Bobbie, I want to have sex with you sometimes.'"

"How does that feel?"

"Not very romantic. But I don't know what else to say."

"What are you feeling right now?"

"I'm really angry. She never lets me decide anything. Sex or anything else, for that matter."

"How does she stop you?"

His nostrils flared. "She doesn't, I guess. But it just makes me so mad! Goddammit, I'm just tired of being so helpless all the time!"

"Can you let yourself have that?"

"No! It's wrong! I feel like a horrible person for being this way. I should know what I want, and I don't!"

"So, I hear every want or need you have is met with shame."

"Yes! And you know, it was the same with Pat. Somehow, I wind up here every time. I feel like I'm back with my mom!"

"You got that right. You keep picking partners who fill the role of your mother. It's the only thing that feels like home to you."

I watched him wrestle with confusion. I decided to take a step further, risky though it might be. I continued, "What your mother did 'in' to you, you learned to do 'out' to everyone else. You've internalized your mother's energy, and now it's the only way you know how to live the relationships in your own life. Your anger at Bobbie for not doing what you want is exactly what your mother did to you."

His face had the fierce panic of a cornered animal. I held his gaze.

"David," I said, "you've never had a relationship with a woman where you didn't make her the enemy."

Guidone's simple words struck like thunder. I cried out in anguish, slumped to the floor, knees cracked on the carpet. I was hurled into a putrid pit of despair and self-loathing. I saw how I was, and I didn't like it. It was ugly. I was ugly. A lifetime of torment, and I had been spewing it out to everyone in my orbit. I hated myself for being that way and I hated myself for hating myself. I collapsed into pain with a strangled cry. I felt the room shake.

As if from a great distance I heard the words, "Hold on to yourself, David. Stay here. This is the deepest, darkest place you will ever go. This is what it was like for you as a child. This is what home tasted like. I call this the 'death layer'. It feels like death, because as a child it would have been death to be abandoned, to be deprived of mother's milk. You're reliving the terror of having your own feelings in the face of her great selfishness. What it felt like to be David every hour, every moment of your life."

I heard a howl of anguished pain pierce the air. Realized it was coming from my own throat. "Breathe, David, breathe," came to my rescue. "Don't be afraid to stay here. This won't kill you. It only feels like it. Stay here, don't disappear. Don't go away. Just sit here and experience it. You can do it."

Time folded up. I dissolved into a dark and bottomless loneliness which I recognized as my childhood cage. I was terrified that I would be trapped here, the weight crushing down upon my body forever.

"Stay here. Stay. Right. Here." Guidone kept repeated the words. I stayed. It was nearly more than I could bear, but I

124

stayed.

Suddenly in a flash I knew: this exquisitely terrible pain was all mine. No one ouldn take it away. I want it! I don't want to throw it away, fling it out into space, get rid of it. I mean, I do want to, but I won't. I won't be numb anymore. I want my feelings back. I want to feel!

Guidone's voice came softly, "I have so much compassion for you, David, the way you had to wound yourself to save yourself. You didn't deserve the treatment you got. No child does. Stay, just stay right here. This is what it was like to be the child David."

Now I tried to wriggle free. Even as I brought the beautiful words in, I tried to throw them back out. I can't have my life. I'm not worthy of this. I don't deserve it. You're tricking me, Guidone. My mom is right. I don't believe you. This can't be true.

Gradually, correct space and time returned. I felt as if I was crawling back into my body with this new awareness, crowding in to make room for it, pushing the garbage out. Now that I'd found it, I didn't want to lose it. I fought my way back into the world, claimed my safe abode.

As if from a deep well, an overflowing joy coursed upward through my body and spilled out my throat, a madly gleeful laugh filled the room. The sweet release of something that had been dammed up for a lifetime.

I opened my eyes. I'd been gone eons. The late afternoon light was pouring through the garden window onto the Oriental carpet in intricate patterns as if diamonds had spilled out on it. I felt suddenly larger, higher than the world.

Out of the corner of my eye I saw a box of tissues floating through the air.

"Oh, thanks, Guidone," I laughed. "But no. No, thanks. I want to keep these tears. I want 'em right here!" I realized my face was soaking wet.

"You'll never wash your face again, eh?" was the snark reply. Perfect. We laughed together now.

"That's right," I cried. "I've earned 'em, I'm keeping them! Hahaha!"

The corners of Guidone's mouth turned a wry grin. "I understand."

In the front garden, sitting on the bench under the Japanese maple, its red leaves fluttering in the sunlight, everything seemed more alive, vibrant. Sounds were crisp and sparkling, the flowers intimate and alive, the trees taller, greener.

Ambling slowly through my own little garden at home, I felt like Adam walking into a fresh and intimate world. My world. I looked up to meet the sky. I expanded to fill every corner of the great dome over my head. The world suddenly shook with laughter, until the release of joyous tears brought me down gently to the rich and fragrant earth.

The session had begun with anger. My fury at Guidone for not saving me. For not making the pain stop. For not chasing my mother out of my head once and for all. I finally erupted, expressing what had been building inside me for weeks...months...a suppressed rage...which squeaked out of my throat in a hoarse whimper.

"Guidone, I'm angry with you."

"I hear you, David."

That was it. Not 'Don't you dare be angry with me!' Not clamming up and retreating in a sulking huff. No punishment, no death by a thousand slights. No abandonment.

I was thrown off balance so I went back to my go-to habit.

"Well, I'm not that mad. Just a little bit, I guess, about a few things."

"Wait, what? I don't get any of your anger? You're holding out on me, David. I can handle your anger. You know that. I'd much rather have your anger than your disappearing act. You don't have to hide your feelings from me."

"Well, yeah, then I've been kind of pissed off at you. For not saving me."

"I hear you."

"Then why don't you?"

"Believe me, if I could save you, I would."

"Well, you're a pretty rotten therapist then, aren't you?" I
sneered. We laughed. "But yeah, I guess I knew that. I've got to
save myself."

"It's true. It's funny, you know, I think a lot of the patients
who come to see me don't really want to get better, they just
want me to make them more comfortable in their neuroses. They
don't want to change. They don't want to confront their stuff, do
deep soul work, self-examination. They're terrified of what they
might find. They'd rather keep their craziness."

"There are times I'd sure like that," I admitted.

"Me, too, sometimes. But I think after all the work you've done,
to go back you'd have to walk back through everything you've
learned, every little piece of growth. It'd take too long. But I
understand the temptation. The old way is like a comfortable
coat, even though patched-up and threadbare it's familiar."

"Yep, that's a good way to think of it. I guess I prefer doing
the work to being how I was, dang it. It does feel good to walk
out the other side of a good cry or a good session." I suddenly remembered a scene from an old film. "It's like that line

from Lawrence of Arabia, where Peter O'Toole says, 'The trick is not that it doesn't hurt. The trick is that I don't mind that it hurts.'"

"I like that. I think I'll use it." We chuckled.

"But Guidone, I wanted to ask you..."

"What?"

I gathered my thoughts. "Well, I know I'm the author of my own unhappiness. I get that. And how I dish it out to everyone else, exactly what I got. But how do I not do this anymore? How do I keep from acting out? I don't want to pass my mother's madness on to everybody else. I don't want to be like her."

"You are like her. You can't stop being like her, any more than you could hold your breath forever. It's part of you, right down to the cellular level. Her bones are your bones.

"The one difference is awareness. You've been brave enough to look at your dark shadow. She was never willing to do that. Aware, you can make choices. But you've got to know what you're doing in order to change what you're doing."

The grief of what I have lost and can never regain sometimes overfloods me.

Tears will erupt from some deep ocean till I'm caught up in their wash like flotsam. It used to bother me, thinking there must be something wrong, but not so much these days. I enjoy living in a body that knows when it needs to cry, or laugh, or just be how it is. I try my best to heed its wisdom.

I can see now that therapy saved my life. Am I through? Have I matriculated? No. I can't fool myself about that. I still seek therapy when I feel in need of that special help that nothing else can provide in quite the same way.

And I do have other things that help. Meditation. Walks in the woods. Writing in my journal. Dreams. Slowing myself down to a stillness that allows the faint but unmistakable voice of my innate wisdom to be heard.

Just this morning, for example, it hit me again, as if brand-new. The realization that my narcissism, my pervasive finger-circling-over-my-head it's-all-about-me habit, makes me miserably unhappy—or let's say, it is a hollow, ephemeral happiness like cotton candy or plastic wrap or Facebook likes. When I'm able to put that mask aside and focus outside my narrow world, I discover a vast universe of wonder in everything and everyone around me that's totally unavailable when I'm closed in. That warms me to the core.

My father died too young.

He was the first person in my life to disappear that way. Despite the pain that I felt at his passing, I was grateful for the chance to reconcile with him during the last years of his life. He softened during that time, grew more open and tender. I felt my heart soften toward him as well.

I came to appreciate the good things I had inherited from him. A love of honesty and authenticity. A solid sense of right and wrong. An impish sense of humor. A curiosity about the world. A vivid imagination.

He loved designing, building, creating, playing with ideas then bringing them to life in material form. Tinkering, puttering, dreaming. He loved the natural world, and science, which he used to penetrate its mysteries. And he gave the most intimate hugs.

After his death, my mother came undone. He'd been her bedrock and steady helper throughout life. Without him to keep her grounded, she was like a skittish colt thrashing wildly in confusion and panic.

She lived half a continent away, but we'd talk on the phone sometimes. Her tone would often turn scolding, harsh, almost tyrannical. Trying to console or comfort her was like petting a porcupine; I wound up scratched and bruised. Often after our conversations I'd be crying, pitched once again into the loneliness of my childhood. I had to be careful not to let her in too far.

As time wound on through the years, the hours and days were a torment for her, at first emotionally, then toward the end, physically. None of us, no one in her circle of friends, colleagues, or family, was able to reach her during that time. No one was good enough for her. She stood isolated in a lonely place of her own making. She grew more bitter, angry, and self-righteous, stubbornly unyielding. We stood helplessly by as she become almost feral, consumed by lifelong heartbreak.

Then after a long, painful agony of cancer, she too passed away.

After her passing, I was overwhelmed with grief. I plunged into an abyss of despair more intense than anything I had ever known. I'm not sure I could explain it. I'm still not sure I understand.

But the memory of that time is precious nevertheless. Perhaps only after she was gone, once I was truly an orphan, could I finally allow myself to mourn the loss of all that she had given me, both good and bad, and grieve the loss of her great but wounded spirit.

After her passing, the family had the task of going through her effects. We discovered many things I had never seen before. Old newspaper articles, clippings, photos; paintings, photos, and sketches; recordings, letters, books, CD's, home movies, and precious nuggets of family keepsakes. It was like reading a book about someone I'd never met.

I learned more about her father, Gerhard. I found a copy of an autobiography he'd written near the end of his life. I eagerly pored over this treasure of history, thirty-three typewritten pages about my grandfather's life.

I'd known that he had abandoned his wife and children (my mother along with her younger sister and brother) when my mother was twenty years old. But his autobiography told more of the story. I inserted the puzzle pieces into what I already knew.

My mother had been in college at the time, majoring in psychology. One day Gerhard asked to borrow some of her textbooks, pretending to be interested in the subject. She loved her daddy, so of course was glad to share them.

It was soon after that that he filed for divorce and abandoned his family.

Borrowing her textbooks had been a trick. He wanted to divorce his wife, my grandmother Elsa. But he was the minister of a large congregation, prestigious, respected, pillar of his community. He couldn't obtain divorce without good cause. But if he could show somehow that Elsa was mad, then it would seem like a regrettable but understandable necessity.

Thus, he had used my mother's knowledge of psychology to prove that his wife was insane. She realized to her horror that she had unwittingly been part of his scheme.

Elsa got next to nothing in the divorce settlement. She was

forced to give up her lifelong dream of becoming a singer, take odd jobs to make ends meet, and care for my mother and her siblings for the rest of her days.

My mother never forgave him. The sting of her father's betrayal stuck deeply embedded for the rest of her life. She once told me the story of an attempt to visit him long afterward.

"Twenty-five years later, I decided I was finally ready to reconcile with him. He'd been living just five miles from my house all this time, so I got in the car, drove over there, and started to walk up the front porch stairs. I got as far as the third step. Then, I don't know, it was as if my legs were made of iron. I couldn't move. My body wouldn't behave. I turned around, walked back, got back into my car, and drove off. After that, I never saw him again."

She didn't say what prevented her from knocking on his door, from contacting him again, only that she couldn't do it. And I didn't ask. I wish I had. But she herself may not have known.

After reading the deeper story of Gerhardus' betrayal, putting that together with what I already knew of my mother, I felt I understood her better. She likely spent her entire life wondering at every moment who in her circle of friends and acquaintances would be the next to abandon her. Always looking for some subtle clue that it was about to happen, that someone would suddenly disappear forever. The great wound inflicted by her father taught her that no one could ever be trusted.

And she also learned to preempt that abandonment. If it's about to happen, then let's get it over with! I watched her toss people away like yesterday's trash without so much as a by-your-leave. With the flimsiest of provocations. Friends, even family, no one was immune from her bile. She would denounce some perceived betrayal on their part, then suddenly they were as good as dead to her.

It frightened me. I never felt safe with her, always alert for the hidden signs that I too was about to be abandoned.

There was more in Gerhard's autobiography. He described how, when he was a child, his father John would fly into a rage and beat him black and blue with a fireplace poker. Gerhard never knew when it would happen, or what he had done to deserve it. His mother was powerless to help.

At the end of John's life, he was hospitalized, refused to eat food and so starved himself to death.

And John's father, Gerhard's grandfather, after hard times and business failures had left him miserable and broke, died on the way home from a bar. Drunk, he fell and drowned in a shallow ditch by the side of the road.

This, up until then unknown to me, was the history of my mother's family.

The last part of Gerhard's remarkable story touched me most deeply. A single typewritten page, written several years after the rest of the manuscript, was appended to the folder. It read as a sort of self-analysis of his life.

"Allow me a bit of self-reflection," it begins, "...I confess that I rarely expressed and as a result, rarely received, genuine warm emotion. I found it next to impossible to dedicate myself emotionally to any single individual - not even in marriage or with any of my children ... the resultant incurable loneliness gave way to aloofness and created in me a deep conviction of having to face life alone. This ... gradually engendered an attitude of arrogance which expressed itself in suspicion and sarcasms. I sought refuge in cunning, conceit and evasion. At any rate, I convinced myself at last that close associations and warm friendships were not to be for me. Whatever strange and exciting roads I was to travel I would walk alone, depending only upon myself. Every bond to me was a bond of sorrow and I learned to live on a new isolated terrace."

As I read this, I had the eerie feeling that I had written it myself. It described my own life. Nothing has given me a clearer insight into the genesis of my own character than did this, his last and most honest confession.

Also among my mother's things was a videotaped interview with a holistic healer she had seen for some physical ailments, recorded during their initial session together. The woman asked my mother not only about her symptoms but also about the deeper emotional and spiritual issues that often underlie visible ailments.

"Tell me about your mother," she asked at one point.

My mother gazed upward and her face broke into a glorious sunny expression. "She was a dear," she said wistfully. "I loved her. Poor thing! After our father left, I sent her money every month because I knew she was destitute. Then after she passed away, I went through her things and found every check I had ever written, uncashed. She was too proud to be dependent upon her daughter."

"I see," said the healer. "It sounds like you loved her a great deal."

"Oh yes, I did! I loved her so much. I felt so sorry for her after the family broke up."

"So now tell me about your father."

The corners of her mouth turned down in a scowl. "He was a son of a bitch."

The video was painful to witness. Yet important for me to do so, necessary. I recognized the pain, heartbreak, and impotent loneliness of my own life, mirrored in hers.

In the years preceding her death, in the wake of the healing I had done over decades, I developed a deep compassion for her. My anger and bitterness fell away, no longer necessary. Now that I was protected from her thrashing and flailing, I could see that she had been a victim, too.

I can see the sorely wounded little girl which had been trapped in her skin. She did the best she could. She loved me the only way she knew how, the way she had been loved. I can forgive her now for whatever trauma she may have visited upon me, just as I would wish to be forgiven.

As a psychologist, she had helped many others heal from their emotional trauma. The tragedy was that, in the end, she was unable to heal herself, to find release from her own deep suffering.

Trauma rolls like a great stone down through generations, crushing each new life with its ponderous weight till someone stops the cycle. In my case, I am that someone. I will not carry my mother's pain forward. I will not pass my own heartache and misery on to those in my circle. In healing myself, I do what is in my power to heal the future.

The Weight of Light

I sit alone by the dark
light of my one candle.

Delicious sadness carries me
beyond the umbra of the taper's glow
through the hollow rooms of
my empty house. Eventually
the noble bed claims me.
Let the candle burn.

As I wallow here half asleep,
across the world
a boy in India no doubt awakens
with the rising sun
streaming brilliant through his
lace-curtained window.
As he watches those golden
threads pulling through
the thin smoke of morning's fire

to stitch themselves into the cotton
folds of his mother's purple sari,
he is buoyed, his thin young body
lifting in a rapture.

Meanwhile the thread of this thought
is weaving me across
imagination's wrinkled fabric
to a woman planting rice in China,
singing to bundled tufts of grass
hands lift from basket through air
in one smooth motion and
push into pockets of mud
until her empty wicker vessel
lifts her bodily to the passing clouds.

I wonder why it takes so much courage,
so much effort, simply
to be happy, to allow my still
small seedling to be plucked from basket
into a waiting cradle of warm wet soil.

Further east, someone on the edge of the prairie
opens his eyes in the soft light.
The trees have whispered themselves into
dense fog outside his morning window.
He will toss bedsheets, slip into the forest naked
and walk through the wild wood light as light!

But I step back into his body in time
to snatch the impulse away
before we bring too much joy down
upon our brittle body.
Falling back, then, toward the comfort of my
unhappy pillow, I do not notice the sun
climb behind the thick veil of mist or the
forest gain fresh understanding in the dawn's light
or feel my heart tugging upward,
yearning to rise as a small bubble wants to
lift itself slowly through sweet, thick honey.

148

My Body

My body knows exactly what I need.
I awaken at dawn and we ride,
me and my marvelously competent young steed.

On his brow the sweat will soon appear
as I put him through his paces in the field.
He knows the course much better than the I

which believes it is the I will likely ever know.
I let him lead while I loosely hold the reins
for when I interfere it leads to falls.

Galloping to task he is awesome to behold,
ever-present in a way I've never mastered.
Soon the wood is chopped, water carried.

At dusk it's to the barn, a bowl of oats,
a glass of red, some reading, conversation
then the two of us repair to stable bed.

This is when he truly shows his worth
for in the subtle light his bones display

to my vision all that we are made of:

moons, pixies, frogs and trees, toy soldiers,
puddles, mushrooms, tangled up in stardust
held aloft by innocence and awe.

All these things and many more besides
toss and tumble 'round us in the dark
as the two of us enfold and mesh

and honor what we are to one another.
While we dream in the quietude of slumber,
high above our head we build tomorrow's

constellation on the sable velvet
of the sky, where pips of light display
the shape of all we'll soon become.

When dawn arrives to paint the world in bliss,
we celebrate each other in a song or in a verse
or with a satisfying poem such as this.

Surrender

The hell my cousin thinking
  reciting me a poem
lodged in memory thirty years?
  Now I gotta buy the guy's book
to find out why if he's that good
  he ain't famous.

When David Jauss slides in a box
  through the mail slot I unwrap
and crack him open. I read.
  This is how he comes into my life.

The book disguised itself
  as badly written, a stupidly clever
way to bust the lock on
  my thin skin, sidle uninvited in,
elicit beats I never knew I owned.

I want to raise him a dozen or call,
  make him justify himself, prove he's
 better or worse of a poet.
I'm torn between jealousy I can't write like him
  and fear I will never write like myself.

Onto the floor goes the book,
  tossed down
in desperate outrage!

But I must pick it up again after
  certain phrases echo, sting me with the
hot and pressing logic of a ripped-off scab.

  Ancient secrets spill out through
the unlatched window of my pride,
  remember themselves but still
he comes on merciless, sneaking past
the stairwell into the basement of my despair

where I stand alone in all that
founders in that murky mess,

a place I had forgotten, there
beneath the crushing weight of truth
where nothing shallow, ephemeral,
untrue long survives.
I cry out in beastly pain. I see the heart
I seek is not outside me,
simply beyond my small horizons.

From his borrowed vision grows a new thing
which I build myself, rising from the
putrid ooze of muck like the first sea-blind
creature to crawl on naked land.

Veritas

I find myself once again dancing on the edge
of a hatpin.
I cannot tell how many of me there are,
two at least, the hidden and the show-off,
maybe more. We survive by throwing
all our darkest secrets out into the open air.
We perform for ourselves alone, working best when it
no longer matters what the others think and
no one knows how the story ends.

Audience is carried then in quite the same
uncertainty,
suspended animation as we hang in disbelief
finally landing
on a note of resolution or a failure to resolve.

The room revolves in rhythms which I merely
   mirror to the crowd. We jointly gasp aloud at all we
should have seen coming. I call our bluff,
         confirm our secret wagers
then I ride the liquid riptide of applause as if my tiny bark
   would swamp for the lack of it.

   The spinning venue's heat and roar crack this angel open
allowing fear to seize me by its talons. I yield
to the pain, crying from my desperate depths
   a lowing moan like dying animals.
         O how I savor of this sacred time alive
      no more aware of any struggle,
   long since lifted to the wind.
     Soon it folds me all
         together   tangled.
   I become an audience of one
      watching myself move to music
                  only I can hear.

Stepping down I meet myself coming up,
the venue sudden looms larger than cathedral,
        walls ballooning out, ceiling tossed up to the sky
yet everything is hazy like a hasty sketch
        drawn on shifting sand from faulty memory.

Sitting back at table as my body tries to shrink away
    from the terror of my nakedness,
I sooth it with these words:
        This is how you love. This is how
you know your aim was right all along,
        true and to the center of your stage.

Puffin

When angels drop to earth I'm sure
they do so with no more boldly affectionate grace
than did a certain Maine Coone cat,
stretching up to our front door
one May morning from heaven
knows where, well-groomed, fresh,
insistent that he had long known us.
Well, we opened the door as directed
he came rightfully in, padded politely to the far
pantry to use the loo, then back to
resume with us this wide conversation.

Maybe he'd lived here before, who knows.
Days drifted to weeks, years. We performed
our feline staff duties as we had learned them
while he grew us large enough to contain
his generous and encompassing love.

Came a day we saw that even deities

must bow to fate. He was no exception.

Puffin—this is what we'd named him—moved

through the terrible weeks

encased in a yielding protection invisible to us.

The day he came again

into the pantry, thin, withered, unable to stand,

I helplessly watched him collapse to the floor.

Not willing to guess how close we were,

I gathered him to my bosom, carried

him to the sofa, draped his body over mine

where he laid across my belly like a limp towel.

I still felt the faint in and outing of life.

Then a moment went by and with a sigh,

a soft gesture like the closing of a flower at night,

it seemed he fell gently warm down,

down into my body.

There we were.

It took my eyes a moment to realize,

then they sent their wet acceptance,

surrender, to wash across the hollows of my face.

Now we rise together, float across the floor into
the woodshop. I lay him quietly on the workbench,
rummage through the lumber pile for a suitably
stout and solid walnut plank on which to lay him.
Then out to the garden where I place
plank and vessel on the earth and we dig.

Early every April yellow daffodils
riot in profusion with a heavenly hosannah,
while sitting strong upon his bones
they lift their eager faces to the sky.

Turning In

Wee hours spent in restless turning
Tossing, wide-eyed useless yearning
A thousand imps inside my head
Enough! I cry, jump out of bed

Stumble to the study where
I seek a poem for comfort there
I Shelly, Rumi, Frost awaken
Find their wisdom has been taken

Not a single book I read
Seems to give me what I need
None I pull down from the shelf
Knows me better than myself

My sleepless spirit starts to sink
Until I spy a pen with ink
My eyes then come to rest upon
Some paper to be written on

I coax the words into a form
Will comfort me until the morn
The words will bring me what I seek
If I allow my heart to speak

Wisdom comes when I but ask
Writing toward it is my task
I find my purpose not on shelf
But in friendship with myself

I have what I sought in tomes
Upon this page in my own poems
Back to bed, the covers on
To soundly slumber till the dawn.

Dragonfly

Bullet-like I flit and dart,
Hover, swoop and glide.
Where will I go next, you ask?
Wherever I decide.

I am the Breaker of Illusions.
I am not what I seem.
Through my glassy wings you glimpse
The truth as in a dream.

Never underestimate
The power of one so small
To reveal what is hidden,
Render visible to all.

I can see through walls and lies
That is my special art.
Past your skin my thousand eyes
Will penetrate your heart.

Phildelphia

O Philadelphia

Verse 1

Oh, my Philadelphia, love is in your name

You grew from Pennsylvania to the world

You remade your people in the banners they unfurled

In future earth will never be the same

Verse 2

You composed a symphony which time cannot erase

I am lifted by my faith in that ideal

I pledge my honor, fortune and my life to make it real

To feel your morning sun upon my face

Chorus 1

Citadel of freedom, I have walked your streets for years

Often with my head up in the sky

With my feet upon the ground, I have grown the wings to fly

Far beyond the prison of my fears

Verse 3

Philadelphia, you have borne a son

My life is the seed that you have sown

One which I've replanted within everyone I've known

That it may live on when I am done

Chorus 2

Broken bell of freedom, flawed though you may be

You still beat all the other games in town

Where the content of our character becomes the common ground

If we refresh our tree of liberty

Verse 4

Philadelphia is calling out to me

Penn's deep woods are calling to me, too,

From mountains carved in jade with crystal waters running through

Standing by the vastness of the sea

Verse 5

Oh, my Philadelphia, the city with a view

To a future where we live in brotherhood

Faith and hope and courage all may serve to make it good

But only love can make it true

   Yes, only love can make it true

   Only love can make it true.

Raymond Starzmann
1945–2019

Presidential Scholar | Historian | Reenactor

**Portraying President Harry Truman near the
Truman Farm Home in Grandview, Missouri**

Everyone was Raymond's best friend, and he was theirs. He didn't much care for music, with one exception. Elton John's "Philadelphia Freedom" deeply touched his fiercely democratic heart.

Philadelphia was his birthplace, as well as the cradle of this bold experiment we call democracy. So in honor of Ray's warm and encompassing heart, I wrote this song to celebrate the virtues of fairness, decency and brotherly love that he so cherished.

Philadelphia

Music and Lyrics by David Bayard

Nothing Is Lost

Nothing is lost
    every tear makes a river
washing in waves to the sea
    whose tufted white clouds so pregnant with rain
receive the gift of our grieving.

Nothing is lost,
    every death forms a cradle
a creche for new life to begin
    as each fallen tree will surrender of its body
to earth to build soil again.

Nothing is lost
    in wrestling with angels.
No wound from that struggle is fatal.
    Just as a spark is spent building fire
every scar grows to new wisdom.

Nothing is lost
   in the blackness of night
which the dawn will fail to remember.
   As the sun ever shines beyond the dark clouds,
each experience glows in the dark.

When spirit is tossed
   like a bark in rough seas
when despair is our only companion
   when heartbreak and pain and tossing in tides
is beyond our reach to explain,

Nothing is lost.
   Within nature's realm,
In rhythms eternally fluid,
   resplendent in mystery and infinite bounty,
lies a heart in which all things are cherished.

Steady

Once upon a long time ago, far away where the hinge of the world's gate swings open, there lived a small child filled with inconsolable sadness.

One day he decided to turn himself into a leaf. If I'm a leaf, he thought, I can just let the wind carry me wherever it will go.

He was light enough to leap onto the first wild gust. He soared free and dreaming over the earth to distant lands, gliding on the glad currents of the sky, dazzled by the many strange and wondrous sights he beheld.

But he soon realized he was helpless, caught in the chaotic whirl like all the other leaves and seeds and broken twigs which had been flung into the sky, tossed and tumbled in the wild roar and tumult of life.

When the gusty breezes finally settled, he felt himself twirl in dizzy circles to the ground. As he lay there exhausted, he realized he was still filled with the same empty sadness.

So he decided to become a bird. That way, he thought, I cannot be caught in the fickle wild wind. I can go wherever I want to go.

He launched himself once again into the clear blue horizon. He soon learned to steer his way within the flow to swoop and glide and soar wherever he wished. He pumped his way to the top of a magnificent mountain of air, perched himself atop its rising bubble of warmth and coasted serenely into the far distance.

But a dark smudge of purple cloud suddenly appeared on the far horizon. Soon it began to swallow the sky. The swift and terrible tempest engulfed him in flash and bang, flung him about in tumultuous tumbles, pelted him with rain, sleet and hail. He was no match for the power of the storm. It tossed him roughly to earth in a crumpled heap, feathers scattered, wings twisted, body bruised.

And he was no happier than he had ever been.

After the storm passed, he struggled to his feet and shook out his wings. Then I'll become a mole, he thought. I'll just sit snug in my own little burrow while the storm and thunder rages far above. And so he did.

With his sharp claws he dug deep into the pungent earth. He explored the nests and burrows of all the other animals, homes they had excavated deep underground, safe and snug from the weather raging above.

He tried to learn the secret tricks of their life, to discover for himself all that they knew of becoming happy. But he soon became bewildered in this stuffy, stifling world of eternal night. He could not decipher the strange hieroglyphics on the walls, understand the babble of language, or find his way along the tortuous twists and turns of the limitless labyrinth. He became lost and frightened. At last he collapsed in despair onto the dusty sediment.

He was still filled with an infinite sorrow.

Soon he grew tired of his own wailing and wallowing. He decided to become a butterfly. I'll float up to the surface and fly away, he thought. I'll be too small for storms to knock about, and I can flit about just as I please. I'll finally be happy and free!

He unfolded his magnificent wings and fluttered into the freedom of a fair summer sky, eager to explore the world. He skimmed over luscious gardens resplendent with fulsome flowers. He flew down to sample each and every one until he was thoroughly sated with their luscious nectar.

But one morning, his feathery feelers deeply intrigued in a honeysuckle, he felt a sudden urge to fly up, up, up into the heavens and off toward the low southern sun which had day by day been dipping ever closer to the far horizon.

He came to the end of the world where the earth fell away and the sea began. On he flew, compelled by some strange and irresistible longing. His wings became wet with salt spray, his eyes stung, his flight faltered, and his frail body presently tumbled down, down into the briny foam of the sea.

The ocean sloshed him wildly about in its tumbling surf. Hour after dizzying hour he thrashed in the tumult of the sea, desperate to keep himself afloat. At long last he felt himself lifted wave by now gentle wave onto the soft sand of a broad shoreline.

Once his wings had dried and he had lifted his limp form into the warmth of the sun, he realized he was no longer interested in becoming other creatures. The metamorphoses had not made him happy. Throughout his adventures the same deep and abiding sadness which had ever been his had remained unchanged.

So he turned himself once again into the young, innocent, vulnerable child that he had been so long ago.

And there he sat till the sun began to dream of sleep and dozed itself softly down the steep wall of blue. The sea sent her wide waves whispering across the beach, then sliding back to water with a gentle sigh as if the movement were her rhythmic breath. With each new arrival, the boy felt his toes dig deeper into the warm sand.

In the sea-breeze of evening a leaf tumbled past him on its way to the ocean. It was caught by the swell of the out-going tide, in which it appeared, disappeared, then reap-peared as its migrated out upon the retreating waves.

A lone gull above the silvery sea coursed back and forth before the crimson of the evening sky, every so often crash-ing down upon the startled water seeking its evening meal.

A butterfly landed on his arm. He wondered where it had

come from, over what great distances and through what arduous adventures it had travelled before it came so gently to rest upon his sunlit wrist. Its velvety wings opened and closed like the leaves of a book whose wisdom was being savored over and over.

The boy knew that he could become any of these creatures again if he wished, and any of a thousand others. And that he no longer wished to.

But his sadness remained. He reached inside and brought it out into the salt-fogged air. He held it in his hand, examined it, felt its contours, caressed it.

It was the same sadness which had always been his, but now there was a difference. Now it was his own special sadness, which belonged only to him, and to which he in turn belonged.

Belonging. He rolled the fresh word round and round about the inside of his mind.

He watched the dim red sun sink toward its bed beyond the far rim of the world. Soft waves shooshed across the sand to wash under his feet, then retreated as the next line of froth flowed its wet way forward. He felt cradled in the dreamy ebb and flow of the soft sea's embrace.

As time slid effortlessly away, his toes sinking ever deeper into the sifted sands, a soft breeze rubbed its hands gently across his back. The great cathedral of sky turned russet, then violet, then gold.

There he was.

Neither leaf, nor bird, nor mole, nor butterfly. Neither happy nor sad, nor empty nor full. Simply being, at rest within the vast and fathomless mystery.

I'm coming home.

Home has always been here. It was me who had to leave in order to save myself. Now I'm back.

The words "inhabit your realm" recently found their way to my inner ear. And that's what I've been doing. An entire kingdom with endless fiefdoms and a magnificent mansion of many rooms, each unique and resplendent, has been here waiting. And me abroad in foreign lands, exiled from my own domain!

But when I seek this place, I find it has been patiently eager for my return. It has been awaiting my arrival in the ever-present rhythms of my own heartbeat. It has faithfully preserved the innocence, passion, and sense of wonder which I had been born with, tucked away safely in a cozy corner all this time.

I'm older now but I don't feel old. Sure, my bones creak and groan like the rigging of an old ship and my face has deep arroyos sculpted in. But the creaking gives my body a nice lived-in feel and the creases help drain rainwater off my face.

I feel very little different now from when I was a child. It's as if time is curving back along the length of my life, carrying me full circle. I am reliving many of the joys that were mine back then. Stargazing. Cloud watching. Building things. Writing. Climbing trees. Walking in the woods. Making music. Communing with birds, bees, and buttercups.

And I finally found the girl with rocket feet.

It turns out she'd been zooming and swooping right next to me for a long time. I had been so intent on finding the perfect partner that I hadn't recognized her. Once I caught on, I began paying closer attention. She was kind, warm, gentle, understanding. I was much in need of those qualities.

After a time it occurred to me that I liked her. Very much. One day, I gathered myself up and told her.

She said the feeling was mutual.

We zoom around a lot together now. She's not my perfect partner and I am not hers. I think Perfect Partner is a myth.

But we fit together well. Where she has hollows, I have just the right shape to fill them. Where I have parts and pieces missing, well, she has equal but opposite parts that match.

If we get in trouble, we've learned to navigate the slippery ever-changing landscape of us. We hold firm in our integrity;

we bend like willows. We stand up for what we believe; we abandon absolutes. We grind together like two rough stones; we have smooth sailing on calm waters. We have our moments apart; we have joyful joining together. We talk; we listen. She's on my side. I'm on hers.

Sometimes when I'm with her, I think my heart may just burst open like a tender flower.

Long ago my mother read "Winnie-the-Pooh" to me. During the tortuous time when she was in her last bed, two thousand miles away, I read it to her over the phone from the very same book, now faded, tattered, and well-loved. Even from a distance I could feel her expression soften, a contented smile blossom on her face. I was glad I was able to give her that gift. I was glad I was able to connect with her in the ways that had become possible in the final years of her life. I was glad I could nurture her in some small way.

I think about Pooh myself sometimes. When I'm stuck on some thorny problem, I wonder what he would do. He always knew, except when he didn't, and even then he could always ask for help.

When he asked Piglet, that was the best, because Piglet thought Pooh knew everything there was to know. Then when Pooh thought about it, he realized he sort of did. He would reach down inside where the something that he knew was waiting. Then he would see that he already knew it. And he had figured it out all by himself (with Piglet watching, of course, thinking "That Pooh, he always knows what to do!" but you and I know he didn't). It made Pooh bear feel as if he were indeed a Very Wise Bear.

Which reminds me. Remember when I wrote to my future self, asking him--I mean, me--to come back in the Time Machine to save me? Well, I asked Pooh if he could figure out why I never showed up.

Pooh looked at me real funny, tilting his head as if to say, "What? You don't get it?" I sat there for a very long time with him looking at me and my puzzled face looking back. Then it came to me.

I was the Time Machine!

What I was doing then, what I am doing now by writing all of this stuff...well, that's what a Time Machine looks like. I've been taking this Gadget of Words and Memories and carrying myself all the way back to him, I mean me, who was sitting there waiting, and I am finally saving him by this writing. Except I couldn't know that, then. Why not, you ask?

Well, Silly Reader, because I hadn't written it yet! That's the Time Paradox. Even if I could do everything, which I can't, I couldn't do it all at the same time. I had to wait until it happened. But now that it has, it is right on time.

So here I am now and here I am then, the same me. I just couldn't see it because time was in the way of my eyes. That's the way the universe works, I think, though I'm still trying to get my Sea Legs so I can walk in this New Way of Being.

Like right now. I'm sitting at the long desk with the walnut top that my dad made for me, in my bedroom, in my house, on Bethel Park Road, in Pennsylvania, in the world, in the universe. And I'm also sitting right here, writing to you. This is really the same page that I started typing on so long ago, using the same Royal typewriter with the letter ''L'' that sticks and which still makes the same clacky-click noise that it made back then when I said hello to you, way back at the beginning when my eyes were closed and it hurt so bad all the time.

I don't worry so much these days about getting lost and drifting away from myself. There's always a thread I can follow back.

Come on, let's go out to the side yard and find the tallest pine tree there is and climb all the way to where the trunk is no bigger around than your wrist, way, way, way up to the very top where you can see the whole forest all at once, where life and death and beauty and pain and joy and love are all just waving around free in the wind and it's all right there. And you can fly away any time you want to. On your two little rocket-feet.

Or even just your own wings.

I Once Knew the Stars

Rigel, Altair, Procyon, Fomalhaut,
names like ancient runes,
these were all my faraway friends.
Egyptians, Greeks, Romans and all the faiths of Abraham,
my heroes floated deep in space pinned upon
a velvet firmament, displayed to a young boy
rapt in wonder on a Pennsylvania lawn.

Merak, Mirach, Sirius the Dog Star, brightest in the sky,
we were intimate.
I could touch their mystery with my eyes,
their endless fires with my heart.

Aldeberan, Riga, Polaris the Pole Star,
great and small, young and old, colors telling ages:
red giants aged as fine merlot, hot blue teenagers
in blazing leather jackets, mature white dwarfs,
stolid middle-class citizens like our yellow Sol.
I got to know their stellar personalities.

Copernicus, Vega, Proxima Centauri, our next-door neighbor.
I drew charts to fold in pocket:
magnitudes, distances, possibilities.
I dreamed of starships, for someday I would
fling on out to meet them,
hanging there burning up my hydrogen beside them,
intoning fiery mantras to the gods that we all were.

Castor and Pollux, the twins, Alioth, Electra,
my stars are now both closer and further,
the four corners of great Orion
scarce larger than a box of breakfast flakes.
Yet Bellatrix, Betelgeuse, Rigel and Saiph are more
light years apart than the distance of my life.
All four float between my thumb and forefinger.

Cervantes, Sadr, Regulus, come measure me,
I am larger than I am.
Heavy now with star-child, dissolving into
the vastness of constellation David in
its wide animal stretch, limbs flung open,
mouth agape in love, tracing out a place between
the Southern Cross and Pegasus to claim my
own prominence, delicious in the void.

Alioth, Algenib, Malmok,
I find that the stars
are exactly where they always were
even though my view has changed a thousand times.

Mizar, Deneb, Atlas, I trust in hidden realms
but which one thus enables me to form my hands
large enough to block the stars
yet see their bright remembered bodies piercing through?
A child is in me too, looking out
at universes yet to be.

Canopus, Arcturus, Capella,
sometimes longing in the dark I cry out
My God, I'm full of stars! How can the whole of my life
be housed within this frail clot of flesh?

Mimosa, Spica, Elnath, Tania Borealis, I come home.
I step with deep memory out the back door
to sink my grateful body down to cool and dewy grass,
relive the dreams I had of you,
and have those dreams again, my stars,
my friends so greatly intimate at distance,
my ancient, my forever family.

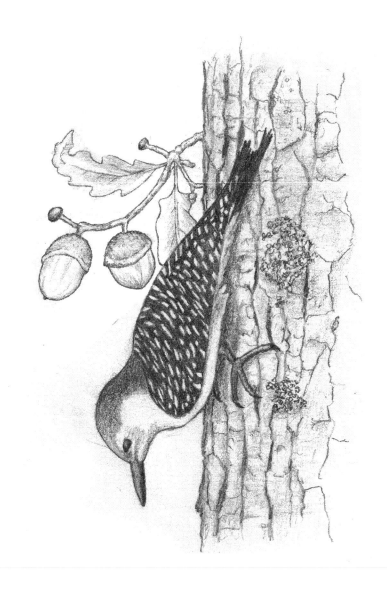

I Understand Now

My unhappiness is not complete
until I join it, whereupon
it transmutes to its opposite.

The yellow flowers in profusion
planted by my mate and me
over many years come alive
independently of us in the
promiscuous riot of spring.

She and I can now share
our sadnesses, bring them to light.
The trees accept them.
The world is full of everything.

Our dog has the runs and
blossoms sing forth,
both things true on the
same brown earth.

The mahogany bench praying to the sun

with its peeling varnish

needs a new coat and

will likely not get it.

Inside the phone may ring

but not now.

The wonder of birds, especially

the woodpeckers, those drillers

into secret wood who eat

the simple suet that I feed them.

They live.

This is all I need.

The Fleur-de-Lis Incident

As I sit quietly, perusing a book I had pulled from the poetry
shelf, my reading is suddenly interrupted by a crash.
Startled, I look up to see that the weighted fleur-de-lis bookend
which had kept the tomes in place has tippled over,

volumes sprawled across the wreckage like ships, cars and
trees tangled against a seawall after a storm. What physics had
pulled them over? Had my choice of material moments earlier
upset the literary balance? Did the books, which had already

been inclined left, decide now was the time to topple authority?
Perhaps there was a dispute among the poets about seating;
Rumi might resent being next to <u>Rag and Bone Shop of the Heart</u>,
which, though alphabetically akin, mixed names and titles, and

Jalāl ad-Dīn parted ways. Or maybe the poems themselves sought
fresh meanings and, weary of their stasis, were switching styles,
mixing metaphors, leaping lines, fixing phrases that didn't work,
changing it up for my next reading. Or could be the words had

grown tired of their stale meanings, lead a voluble revolt,

so that up now agrees to mean down, carrot means stick,

onion means bathtub, napkin means displacement, and Enfield rifle

means I love you. Then they go back to their poems, wait for me to

put the lineup into a semblance of order and see if I'll notice.

I pick up the whole tribe of dogies and replace them on shelf

one by one, preserving the exact order, then write this poem.

I hear them laughing behind me as I write but I slowly realize

they're laughing with me, not at me. We've been in this together

all along, perhaps, the gang of us in sync the whole time

without anyone noticing. So perhaps they'll applaud my

move to break the rules as they did and decide that it's just fine

to wreck the four-line tyranny and sail boldly out on another.

Suddenly On the Porch

Standing by the railing of the back porch
watching, settling like the low red sun pouring itself
out onto the flat table of the world,
it hit me like a tissue-paper hurricane—
there is happiness all around me, peeking out
from the still corners and quiet crevices of the world
waiting for my welcoming hello.
How long had it lain there dormant?

It was like the moment as a child when I realized
my parents had been watching me
play in the sandbox, fully absorbed in timeless action,
putting my trucks and figurines through their paces
in my small world big with magic.
The platoon on a daring raid, moving across the dunes
under covering fire, a devastating attack upon
the backhoe and the skip loader, those hapless
metal moles scurrying to get their foundations dug
before the relentless desert wind sanded them in.
A melee on the high desert!

The two of them limned in the sunlight
hair haloed in gold. Faces lit from within
with expressions unfathomable
yet clearly expecting nothing of me.
I wondered why they watched,
why it warmed me so.

I would not understand what they saw until
this moment, on the porch, when I
felt that bright and eager child
gently with silent rapture step back into
the light and subtle joy of the body
in which long ago their gazes had been
so well invested.

With Mary Oliver

I pull Mary Oliver down from the shelf,
    or sky,
her ghost twinkling black on white.
She speaks in a voice soft and lilting
    of herons and shells,
        small animals, seashores,
    bones and black water all lodged in light.

Folks here think you died, I tell her. She laughs.
      'I have simply been too busy thanking
    God for the gift of sight.
I live carved in nature. Watch!'
        She proves the wisdom of my native
    Penn's Woods deep in emerald,
      marbled with veins of blue water trickling down,
or my friend the California seas crying from the breakers,
      waves caressing shore as if washing the feet of a lover,
or here in Midwestern winter of whispered white silence,
      as I sit before the window on this purple sofa
with the colorful cushions, traveling to places within.

She speaks of once getting lost in the
    land of Big Achievement,
        bondage of the bookstore and review,
    clawed her way back from the precipice
recalling the purpose of light,
    placed her intent on the breathing heart:
        pinecone memories,
    suckling at mother's breast,
larks singing for no reason,
    the glorious slumber of cats,
        frolicking freely in open fields,
    playing piano loud and badly
or sitting on stones by the sea,
    lost without compass in deep meditations—
    as much as to say:
the sacred asleep in the mundane
    so eagerly awakened with a kiss.

Eyes open, she points.
With clear mind unflinching she
    watches, simply watches.
Her heart flits among flowers,
    feathers, froth of beach foam,

witnessing even as the heron
marries the frog in the chapel of its belly.
Transmuting her visions to ink upon paper,
her poems arrive like snowflakes
in blizzards of tufted white blessings.

I find her in a blade of grass.
We surprise one another as if young lovers
or explorers discovering new continents.
We do not bother naming worlds
but idle the day away as if no other task
calls to us than to be present for
the tick-tick footfall of the wren.

On the beach we dance until the sun beds down,
the crescent moon follows with good gravity,
bending low till it belongs gently to the sea.
As I wander through her ripe pages
Inhabiting forgotten hollows of my heart,
I feel her soft breath in my ear.
Sit.
Watch.
Be astonished!

Epiphanies

I wonder if there is something special
about the places where epiphanies detonate.
Buddha's was apparently under a tree
with snails involved,
Muhammed in a cave near Mecca,
Moses on a mountaintop,
Jesus by the shoreline or fishing in the sea
or perhaps as a carpenter
negotiating the heavy weight of timbers,
King at the kitchen table head in hands,
Gandhi in a train station waiting for an arrival
or Lennon sitting on a cornflake
waiting for the van to come.

I wonder if the location itself is critical,
or if these things happen anywhere and the
place later becomes part of the story.

I sometimes wonder too whether I

will ever experience an epiphany,

or whether I've already had one,

or many, or none,

or how and whether I would ever know.

All this wondering happens as I amble barefoot

through the woods without purpose.

Suddenly I stop.

I look down at my feet.

They are busy being feet, sporting the usual

ten toes, the big ones larger as they should be,

neatly lining up their troops to either side,

and all ten animals burrowing into the

soft earth to keep me aloft.

Suddenly I am aware of exactly where it is that

I am standing, and how deeply.

My eyes lift, scraping tree trunks,

as they rise into the leafy canopy

and fall through the cracks to the

open sky.

Home, Child

Chorus

Home, child, home child, when you gonna come on home, child,

Lost away and running wild, when you gonna come on home

Your innocence has been defiled

You've been abused, you've been reviled

Come on home, be reconciled

To the marrow of your bones

Verse I

You have sailed the stormy seas

   Wind-blown by the salty breeze

Searching for antiquities

   Time keeps rolling on

A gypsy in the foreign lands

   Sifting through the desert sands

What you love falls through your hands

   All you've loved is gone

Verse II

Though the wild world you roam
　On the path to find a home
Lost in jungles overgrown
　Searching everywhere
Mud and pain upon your face
　Every bright mirage you chase
Vanishes without a trace
　Into the murky air

Repeat Chorus

Verse III

All your life you've thrown away
　Something precious every day
Thrashed about in wild ways
　No one to blame but you
You see no future, feel no past
　The present moment turns too fast
You long for life to lift at last
　Like the morning dew

Verse IV

You've lost your mom, you've lost your dad
  Along with everything you had
You feel as if you're going mad
  Your face has turned to stone
You look around, there's nothing there
  For you to hold to anywhere
You see bright angels in the air
  But none you call your own

Repeat Chorus

Verse V

Come on back from where you've been
  To the ground where you begin
Mother earth will let you in
  Recognize her own.
Sea and sky become your kin
  You are known beneath the skin
You'll come to realize again
  You are not alone

Verse VI

Climb up to the mountain peak
  Stinging winds caress your cheek
Hear ten thousand voices speak
  Beneath a crystal dome
There's no path to lead you back
  Your house is but a hollow shack
But there is not a thing you lack
  Sing yourself a home.

Repeat Chorus

Home, Child

David Bayard

David Bayard

2

into the mur – ky air | Home, child, home_____ child

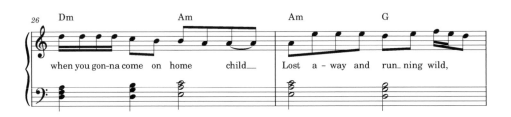

when you gon-na come on home child___ | Lost a – way and run_ ning wild,

when you gon-na come on home? Your | in – no – cence has been de – filed, you've

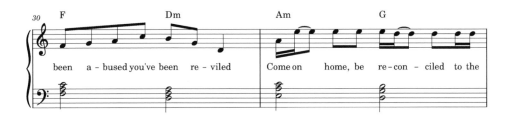

been a – bused you've been re – viled | Come on home, be re-con – ciled to the

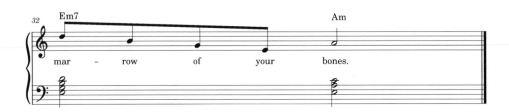

mar – row of your bones.

Mandala

You've talked a lot and joked,
skated round the periphery of heart.
   Have you found your way toward
what cannot be said?

   Can you speak the wordless gesture
of the deeper body
   as your many voices babble busy
like riffles in a stream?

I seek the center point
   of my mandala.

In my hands a healing compass turns
   in spirals round the heart
where every ending reaches back
   to meet a ripe beginning.

I learn to cherish what has always been,
   become that thing again,
as timeless as a child's balloon with child
   attached, floating off in wonder.

Fill the Sails

Fill your empty sails as
    No one else can do.
Blow the winds your way.
    That's within your power.
Any star you steer by is
    the brightest in the sky.

    Mesmerize your Muses.
Treat 'em to a pint o' rum,
    Let 'em hold the rudder
Of the small and sturdy bark
    Which awaits upon the shore
Of your right passion's ocean.

Do not go back to cobbling
    shoes for others.
If this has been your lot
    then rebel.
There are other ways to be.
    Pack your bags.
Give your notice.
    Chart the breathing tides
Of heart as yours has yet to be.
    Go to sea.

It's been raining for days now, a slow, gentle, warm-front rain heralding the turning of the season. I wake this morning to the soft tickling on skylight.

I gaze out the window. Against the backdrop of black trees on the skyline I see the drops falling. Too slowly. Something's the matter with time... My sleep-fogged head, I think. I'm not awake yet. Or maybe time eases up as we age so we can enjoy the newness of things as we did in our youth.

But wait. I am not dreaming. The raindrops are larger, slower, drifting sideways in the wind. It is snowing again. A last stand by toothless winter, a joke typical of the impish Midwestern weather.

Three years have passed. I have a sense of wonder at what they have held for me, held out to me, allowed me to birth. I get up, dress, go downstairs. The cat follows. I don an overcoat this time, for outside it is barely above freezing. I walk into the woods. The cat follows.

Stepping along the trails, skirting puddles in the low spots, I feel my father's spirit keeping company. It was his loan of cash years ago enabled the purchase of this woodland acreage. I whisper gratitude to him. I can almost hear "You guys deserve it!" floating back through the contented trees.

I surprise the deer, as I do most mornings, but their alarm is faint and feeble. They're used to me. They gather a few feet away and watch attentively as I pass.

My mother is here, too, I'm sure, though I can't tell where she might be. I murmur my gratitude for her gift of writing, the love of playing with words in making new worlds, passed no doubt from her body to mine while still within the womb.

I amble through the forest. It enfolds me. Trees stride past as if I were the one rooted. They tip their branches in glad hello. My shoes slip alongside the multicolored leaves and slide wetly on the path. The air is dank, deep, so intimately close I feel part of the sky.

I see that home is not a place, but a journey to be joined. These quietly murmuring thoughts reach out to wrap around me. The way my feet guide the vessel of my body along the gentle path makes it seem as if I'm following a holy procession, some age-old ritual composed of me and everyone who lives, or ever did, and all bright things to come.

The snow has let up. It was never serious. I breathe.

As I approach the Thai spirit house facing our abode, perched on its shelf of tree trunk, I wonder which kindred spirits might be gathered inside today. We do not, as the Thai people do, place flowers and gifts of food on the platform outside the tiny door to entreat happy ghosts to visit. I like to imagine they're here regardless.

I stop, stand, steady myself on the spirit house's tiny handrail, give my blessing to those who may be gathered therein, or hereabouts, or anywhere in the world that welcomes us home.

Notes and Gratitudes

I wish to thank those who have generously given of their time, resources, and attention to assist me in the making of this book. Without their support, encouragement, and generosity, I doubt it would have been possible.

Here, in no particular order ~

~Jadyn Vanoy, whose chalk drawing and lettering for the front and back cover have a freshness and vibrance which, much as I tried, totally eluded me. Thanks for being willing to help, Jadyn, and I hope it was as much fun for you as it was for me!

~Yasin Bekar, whose hand-lettered calligraphy on ceramic plate appears in the frontispiece photograph and whose sensitive work makes a great introduction to the theme of "Home, Child". Yasin can be reached at ybekar02scienceteacher@gmail.com.

~Abby Bland, whose poetic eye, ear, and heart were immeasurably helpful in pruning the dross and drivel from the writing to clarify my intentions.

~ The Poetic Underground of Kansas City. Thanks to Abby Bland and the many others who help foster this "brave space", a stage for emerging poets and artists to hone their performing skills before a supportive and appreciate audience. It was this safe platform which allowed my own spoken-word poetry to blossom.

~Melissa Ferrer-Civil for her incandescent support of poets and musicians at the Tryst venue in Kansas City.

~Deborah Shouse, whose fierce editing clarified and concentrated my writing, even though she had to kill a whole lot of darlings to get there.

~Emily Iorg, whose editing skills were a set of eyes outside my own head which saved me from many blunders.

~Sarah Sattler, whose voice coaching—how to put this—the music in her heart was so clear that I couldn't help but follow her lead and sing out with my own.

~Amory Bottorff for musical, performing, and collaborative help in ways far to numerous to list here.

~Josh Matthews, whose music instruction cracked new worlds open and brought me musically up to date for the twenty-first century.

~Sol Anzorena and Tom Grotwald for their musical and artistic assistance, and for their warm friendship.

~Weiqi Cheng, Sol Anzorena , and the many other artists who have given me tips, techniques, and encouragement in creating the artwork for the book.

David Jauss, for permission to use his name in the poem "Surrender." The poem "Slow River", from his book <u>Improvising Rivers</u>, was the one which so inspired my cousin. This in turn inspired me, as has the rest of David's incisive and heartfelt poetry. He can be reached at <u>davidjauss@sbcglobal.net</u>, and his books can be found on Amazon. com.

~Tom Jacobs of the Timber Creek Retreat House, who has been a balm for my spirit throughout the long and difficult work of spilling my heart onto the page.

~Ben Neal of the Mystic Poet's Society for his support, for welcoming me into the Society of poets, and for his help with the book launch event for <u>Come Home, Child</u>.

~To the many therapists and counselors who shall be unnamed here, who have with skill, courage, and unflinching honesty worked with me over the years to gather and honor my authentic self. Thank you for helping me to save my life.

The character of Guidone is a fictional persona, a made-up pastiche of the several psychotherapists and counselors with whom I have worked over the years. The name comes from the military designation for a flag bearer, or head of a troop column, who is known as the "guideon". I added the 'e' at the end to make it sound more like a real name. Thus, the character was born.

I purposely made Guidone's gender indefinite, giving no clues as to whether the character was male or female (this was not as easy as it first appeared to be!), because I have worked with therapists of both genders over the years. An interesting study for the reader might be to reflect on which gender they had assumed for the character.

About the fonts ~

The prose section that represents David's voice is rendered in a font that I created using an ancient Royal typewriter (circa 1935) which was probably similar to the one I had used as a child. I typed each upper- and lower-case letter, number, and special character onto a dedicated form, then used an online service to create an original truetype font. I named it Beloved Royal.

The poems and songs are rendered in Calibri Light.

All of the other text in the book is rendered in Calligraph421 BT.

David Bayard is a furniture maker, photographer, and writer. He found his way to Kansas City, Missouri, by way of California and originally, Pennsylvania. He lives there on wooded acreage along with his wife and two cats.

His writing draws upon his experiences as an Army lieutenant, rock band performer, homesteader, builder, artist, spoken-word poet, woodworker and craftsman.

He has published three other illustrated books of poetry and stories, all available at

www.skyboyphotos.com.

You can find his fine furniture and woodworking, where his motto is "You Dream, I Build," at

www.samuraiwoodworks.com

Made in the USA
Coppell, TX
04 October 2022

83996050R00146